The Secret
DIARY OF
JOHN MAJOR
aged 47 ¾

Published in Great Britain
by Private Eye Productions Ltd
6 Carlisle Street, London W1V 5RG
in association with Corgi Books

Reprinted 1992

© 1992 Pressdram Ltd
ISBN 0 552 139947

Designed by Bridget Tisdall
Printed in Great Britain by
The Bath Press, Bath, Avon

Corgi Books are published by Transworld Publishers
61–63 Uxbridge Road, Ealing, London W5 5SA
in Australia by Transworld Publishers (Australia) Pty
15–23 Helles Avenue, Moorebank, NSW 2170
and in New Zealand by Transworld Publishers (N.Z.
Cnr Moselle and Waipareira Avenues, Henderson, Au

The Secret DIARY OF JOHN MAJOR aged 47 ¾

Illustrated by
Caroline Holden

PRIVATE EYE · CORGI

November 1990

Thursday

I had just finished my second Shredded Wheat when the phone rang. It was Mrs Thatcher from next door. She sounded very upset about something and told me to come round at once. It was rather inconvenient, because I was just on my way to the office to talk to some men about the hard ecu. They had come over specially from a place called Belgium, and I had been swotting up for days so that I would know what to say to them.

Anyway, I went next door and, to my surprise, there were lots of other people there as well. Some of them were quite familiar because I had seen them on television.

We all went into a big room and Mrs Thatcher suddenly said "It's a funny old world" and started to cry. So did everyone else. We always do what she does. What had happened was that a man called Heseltine (he is often on the telly, too) had been really horrid to Mrs Thatcher, and she told us all that she'd had enough. I tried to think of something to say but I couldn't think of anything.

Then everyone started to leave, looking very sad, but Mrs Thatcher called to me: "Norman, I want you to stay behind." "My name's John," I said, when everyone had left. "It's my wife who's called Norman."

"Shut up," she said to me. "You're going to be the next prime minister, do you understand?"

Friday

The phone has not stopped ringing. It is Mrs Thatcher telling me what to do. How kind she is. First she gave me a piece of paper with all my policies written out. How could she have guessed? She really is brilliant. I agreed with every word. The Community Charge, the Gulf, Europe, the need for party unity — it was all typed out very neatly, with the best bits underlined in red felt-tip pen. That reminds me, I must get a new felt-tip. The last one leaked in the pocket of my blazer and Norman said the cleaners would never be able to get it out.

Anyway, the last bit was particularly good. It said: "Be sure to say 'I am my own man' as often as possible." I must try and remember that. I have written it in my *Economist* diary, next to my cash-card number.

Saturday

We got all the papers this morning, just in case they mentioned me. They did! There was a big picture of me and Norman walking in the park on page 7 of the *Independent*.

All the papers say I'm going to win, which I knew already because Mrs Thatcher had told me.

Sunday

I have been on television! Three times in one day! All the interviewers asked me the same question — "are you your own man?" Luckily I knew exactly how to reply because Mrs Thatcher had told me what to say. She has thought of everything, as usual!

Monday

This morning I had three Shredded Wheats. No, not really! Although I could have done. It was funny not going off to the office as usual, since I had my new red felt-tip with a special top which won't come off !

But later I had a bit of a fright when Norman showed me something in the newspaper about Mrs Thatcher. Apparently she had told everyone that she was going to be a "back-seat driver". I had hoped that she was going to sit in the front with me!

Tuesday

The greatest day of my life! At 6.00 I was watching television at home with Norman when suddenly it said that I had become Prime Minister. At that very moment, the door opened and there was Mrs Thatcher. "Congratulations," she said. "I've won!" I was so pleased for her. She will make an excellent Prime Minister.

December

Monday

When I woke up this morning, I suddenly realised that I was Prime Minister! I thought I'd play a trick on my wife Norman, so I leaned over and asked her: "Darling, here's your starter for ten: — who is the Prime Minister of Britain?" Do you know, she had no idea! So I told her and then she remembered!

After doing my dental floss, which I do absolutely every morning — oh yes — I went to work downstairs. It is very convenient having the office in your house!

I sat at my desk and got to work with a vengeance! I moved all the biros into one jar, set the desk calendar to the right day and then I wondered what to do next. I decided to have a look at the papers to see what was happening. I was amazed to see how busy I'd been, though some of them were being quite rude about me. They said that when I'd chosen all the people in my Cabinet, I'd forgotten to put in any women. Really they are so hypocritical. Last week they were all wanting to get rid of the only woman in the Cabinet. Honestly!

Tuesday

This morning I had four Shredded Wheat! Or so it said in the paper. For some reason all they can find to write about me is what I've had for breakfast. Why don't they write about something important like the way I've reorganised my desk?

Anyway, I've decided that perhaps I ought to have a lady to help me run the country, but I'm not thinking of the one that you're thinking of ! — oh yes — I am my own man, that's what she always used to tell me. No, I remembered that nice woman who came to interview me when we were having our leadership competition. She was called Sarah

Hogg. She asked me lots of difficult questions, and she seemed to know the answers better than I did! Luckily she is married to a chap who is in the Government. What luck!

Wednesday

Oh dear, it seems I am in the doghouse again. No sooner had I decided to put all the red biros in a different jar to the blue ones, and made a note to ask Norman if she could remember to bring my Surrey Centenary cricket mug to put them in, than the phone rang. It was my friend Chris Patten. He's got a new job too. So much for the nonsense about unemployment! "Hello," he said, "is the Prime Minister there?" "No," I said, "she's resigned. Where have you been?" "John," he said, "we've got a problem. You know that West Indian we sent down to be the MP for Cheltenham?" "Yes," I said sharply. "I'm not an idiot, Chris. His father was the West Indies wicketkeeper." Chris and I are both very keen on cricket, and we often pass notes to each other in Cabinet meetings, asking what the test score is. Then Chris said: "Shut up, John, it's important. They've noticed he's black."

Thursday

This job is not as easy as it looks. Norma Lamont, the Chancellor of the Exchequer, rang me up to say he was worried about the economy. He's been through all the books and it appears that things are really gloomy on the money front.

"Who's fault is that?" I said sternly.

"Not mine," said Norma. "It's the chap who had this job before me."

Memo: I must find out who that is.

Friday

Today is Red Biro Day. I am deciding how to reward Mrs Thatcher. She certainly deserves something special after all the help she has given me. I asked Norman what she thought and she said she always gave book tokens because then people could choose for themselves.

Mrs Thatcher has chosen the Order of Merit which sounds quite interesting. Guess what, Mr Thatcher is going to get a knighthood for Christmas.

"That means you will be Lady Thatcher," I told her when she popped in to look through my papers.

"No. No," she said firmly. "I don't want that title. I want

people to go on calling me what they always have done."

"What's that?" I asked.

"The Prime Minister, of course," she said.

Oh, yes.

Saturday

I am going off to Rome which is in Italy for my very first Euro-Summit. Norman has packed all my best grey suits and my new grey tie.

I was a bit nervous of the thought of being with all those important people but Mr Hurd said everything would be all right so long as I remembered to say the special words which he wrote down in my *Young Economist* diary in nine different foreign languages. Whenever anyone said anything to me I just had to read out: *"Je suis mon homme propre", "Ich bin mein ohne man"* and lots of others.

When I said this to Mr Mitterrand who comes not from Italy but from France he gave me a very strange look and used a phrase which Mr Hurd had not told me: "Et qui êtes-vous?"

Tuesday

At last! The end of the horrid old five pee is in sight. I never liked the old coins, they were too big and if you had a lot of them in your pocket they were very heavy. I used to get holes in the jacket of my grey suit all the time and had to ask Norman to sew them up. I remember her saying to me: "John, if you had a smaller coin, I would not have to go to all this trouble."

She had a point. You see do I listen to women. So now, thanks to me we've got brand new five pee pieces small, neat and shiny! I heard my friend Chris Patten telling Norma Lamont that they are calling the new coin The Major because you don't know it's there. What a tribute!

Wednesday

A big aeroplane took me to America, and I saw a very good film. It was *Total Recall* but I cannot remember very much about it. Never mind. When I arrived I was met by a big black car with rows of seats in it and even a drinks cabinet! I asked for a tomato juice which put me in a good mood for meeting Mr Bush.

Luckily Mr Hurd had told me what to say to him. "Good afternoon. I am not Mrs Thatcher. I fully support your policy on everything. Goodbye."

I am pleased to record that the meeting went well and I noticed that we were almost exactly the same height. Quite an achievement, you must admit.

Thursday

I am staying in a very nice room in a big house with a very pleasant English couple, Mr and Mrs Ambassador. This seems to be a common name for people living abroad.

They even had Shredded Wheat which I ate with maple syrup. Quite interesting, I might take some back for Norman.

All the papers say that I cut a very impressive figure and made a great impact on the President.

Isn't that funny, because that's exactly what it said in the press release which my PR man Mr O'Donnell wrote out.

Friday

Back home. We all went off to this big house in the country for Christmas. It is called Chequers and comes with the job of Prime Minister. How kind of Mrs Thatcher to let us use it.

We played Scrabble on Christmas Day, and guess who won? I put down all seven letters with the word HARDECU.

Norman said it didn't count because it was foreign and it wasn't in the dictionary. We had quite an argument about it — oh yes — I may appear mild but in the end I had to give in and she won the game.

Still we made up and drank far too much decaffeinated coffee together.

Then we stayed up late and watched the Nine O'Clock News.

There were some pictures of myself with an American who I felt sure I had met somewhere before. There was also a lot of film of tanks and aeroplanes. They were talking about a war in a place called the Gulf.

I must ask Mr Hurd about this. I will do it as soon as we get back to work, after the recess or what I call the recession. I tried this joke on Norma Lamont who came for drinks on Boxing Day. He thought it was very funny and in return he told me a joke about a nun and a cucumber which I didn't understand at all.

Saturday

To Downing Street. This is in London. It is all very quiet. I was tempted to go back to work but decided to leave the grey biros where they were in the Sainsbury's yoghurt carton. "All work and no play makes John a dull boy." That's what my father used to say when he was somersaulting in the garden.

Norman came back from the shops and said that there was no one at the sales. She said people were blaming the high interest rates.

I couldn't understand it. If the interest was so high, why was there no one there? Later on Norma rang up with another of his jokes, which he told me was from the *Sunday Sport Book of Cartoons*.

January 1991

Monday

Another year begins. I resolve to stop reading the papers. They are so horrid about me. One even said I had no interesting ideas. Honestly! What about TESSA then — the Tax Exempted Super Saver Account?

This was one of my best which I introduced into my budget last year. What happens is that the small saver with up to say £9,000 to invest over a period of three to five years is guaranteed an interest rate of 4% over the gross ordinary share rate provided that the money is not touched for twenty years. Clever eh?

I have had a lot of letters asking how it works which shows how popular it is. I have sent them on to Tessa at the

Treasury. Whoops! Norma of course. I shouldn't have had that second glass of shandy at lunchtime.

Monday night

Tonight was terrifically exciting, because they'd invited Norman and me to Covent Garden for a special gala show. When we were on the way in our big car Norman told me that it was a very special evening because it was to say goodbye to the biggest star of all time, who she only referred to as "La Stupenda". Imagine my surprise, when after some considerable period of waiting, the curtain came up and Mrs Thatcher was nowhere to be seen. Instead there was an Australian lady who everyone gave flowers to. I decided that I quite liked opera. *Home Sweet Home* is a very catchy tune.

Tuesday

What a lot of nonsense people are talking about this recession. Somebody was saying to me the other day that things have got so bad there are no longer any advertisements in the newspapers. Well I spent a considerable period of time this morning looking at them. And they were full of advertisements, nearly all of which were for a building society. They showed a picture of a man with grey hair and glasses. He is called Tessa, which is an odd name for a chap. The funny thing, as I said to Norman, when she was ironing my grey handkerchief (which I have to match my tie), the man in the advertisement looks quite like me. When my friend Chris Patten dropped in this morning to tell me about the latest opinion polls — down a bit, worse luck — I showed him the advertisement which I had cut out from several of the papers, and I said: "Surely this proves that things aren't as desperate as everyone says." But Chris gave me one of his funny looks and joked: "They must be pretty desperate if they're using a picture of you."

Wednesday

Very busy morning spent looking round the office for an appropriate spot to pin up the Alliance and Leicester advertisement which proves that there is no such thing as a recession. I eventually decided to put it in between my favourite colour photo of Mrs Thatcher and the very nice calendar I was sent by the accountants Touche Waterhouse. This year they have had the clever idea of each month having a specially done watercolour of one of their main offices in different parts of the world. This month, which is January, they have their office in Hong Kong. I have to admit I've had a peek at some of the other months, and they are all a bit alike, even April which is the one in Kuwait.

Thursday

It is funny I mentioned Kuwait yesterday, because today I was told by Mr Hurd that I had to go there. Or at least quite near, to a place called Saudi Arabia. I have to go to talk to a lot of our soldiers to boost their morale. My friend Chris came in and said that if that was the idea, wouldn't it be better for me to stay at home. I didn't quite follow him.

Friday

During the morning I spent a considerable period of time in my favourite shop, Milletts. Mr Hurd had told me that if I was going to the desert, I would probably need a special protective suit. I said to him quite firmly, oh yes: "Don't be silly, Douglas, you can't wear a suit in the desert. It's far too hot. You have to wear something like a tee-shirt." Douglas can be awfully dense sometimes, considering that he went to a famous school! In the end I thought it prudent to take two tee-shirts, one of them grey and the other one grey. Who says when it comes to dress that I am not my own man!

Saturday

Here I am in the Gulf! I have had a terrific day. First I went in a tank. Then they took me in a helicopter. Then I went on a ship. I had to make a speech in front of lots of cameramen. I said to them: "Keep up the good work, lads. We are all behind you. That is what Mrs Thatcher would have wanted me to say." They were very pleased and gave three cheers for Mrs Thatcher, which I joined in. Oh yes. Who says she is a hard act to follow? I find it very easy. I've been doing it for years.

Monday

Back in Downing Street, postcode (don't forget) SW1 1PLC. Mr Baker arrived just after the milkman. He looks quite different since he became Home Secretary. He has developed an American accent like a man in a film. They say people grow into their jobs but Mr Baker looked at least seven inches taller and has lost a lot of weight. And all this after not a very considerable period of time!

He said that we should mobilise British troops in the Gulf at once. I was quite miffed and told him it was nothing to do with him. There was only one person who could make that sort of decision — and that was Mr Bush.

Wednesday

Today is the big day we have all been waiting for. The *Daily Telegraph* coloured map of the world arrives! It comes with a note from Mr Hurd saying that I should put it up on the wall behind my desk. He says it will help me to know where all the places are when the war starts. My first key decision comes almost immediately. Should I use drawing pins, or blu-tac? I decide on the latter, as it has always been Mrs Thatcher's favourite colour! When the map is finally put up, I spend some considerable period of time studying it. Iraq is really quite big, compared with, say, Israel. I am glad to see, however, that America is bigger than both of them!

Wednesday night

I get a phone call in the middle of the night on my special grey telephone hotline. It is Mr Bush. Why do Americans never remember that we are asleep when they are awake?! He says that he has had to start the war without me, as he couldn't get through earlier, and he hopes that that's all right. I tried to think of something memorable to say, and luckily it came to me in a flash. "Oh yes," I said, but he had already hung up.

Thursday

We have the first meeting of our new War Cabinet. Me, Douglas, Mr King, my friend Chris Patten and, of course, Norma Lamont from next door. Norma kicked things off in great style by telling a joke about Saddam Hussein and a dead camel. We all laughed although I did not get the last bit. Then Douglas turned to me and said: "Well, Prime Minister, what are our war aims?" Honestly, Douglas can be very slow sometimes for someone who's been to Oxford! "We are aiming at Iraq of course," I said firmly, pointing at where it was on the map.

Then I told them that I had had a very long telephone call from Mr Bush in the middle of the night. They were very impressed. "Oh yes," I said, "it went on for some considerable period of time." My friend Chris smiled and said: "About a minute, I suppose." "Oh no," I said, "not that long."

Friday

We have had a lot of letters about the war. It is amazing how many of them forgot to put on the postcode, SW1 1PLC — which you would have thought was pretty easy to remember!

Saturday

Today Norman and I had to go to Chequers (Mrs Thatcher's country house, which she has lent me while I am Prime Minister). First we had to go back to Graylings — that's our real home in the country — to fetch some towels and my pocket calculator, which I left there last weekend. On the way I told Norman about my top-secret phone call from the President of America. "But you're not to tell anyone," I told her, "because it is still meant to be classified." "Don't be silly," she said. "It was on the 9 o'clock news last night." I was very annoyed at this "leak". In Mrs Thatcher's day someone would have had to spend more time with their family over something like this. "If it was a leak," Norman said, "I bet it was your friend Norma. I've never trusted him since that party at Jeffrey Archer's when he and that actress got stuck in the lift together."

Sunday

Today we had to go to church and be photographed. I wore my new grey suit. The service was very nice but it went on for a considerable period of time. The vicar made a special prayer about peace, and he asked for divine help to strengthen all world leaders in their efforts for peace. He then gave me a long hard look. I wonder why? Perhaps he thought my choice of tie (Old Rutlishians — light grey stripe on dark grey background) was inappropriate.

Monday

Norman is still in a sulk with me. While I was eating my Weetabix (2½ today), I told her: "If you go on like this, I shall have to call you Stormin' Norman." This was because of the American in Arabia who has been telling me what my plans are for the war. She didn't see the joke, unfortunately.

Tuesday

Today I have to make a Big Speech in the House of Commons. Mr O'Donnell says that I should speak for some considerable period of time, and that it is very important that I should not just sound like a dalek. "Not that you do, of course, Prime Minister," he added hurriedly. "Oh yes," I replied, "I am my own man. I will obey."

Wednesday

All the papers said that my speech was a great success. One even said I had been quite like Mr Churchill during the war, especially in the bit when I said: "If something nasty happened to Mr Saddam then I for one would be quite pleased — oh yes."

February

Sunday

When I got up this morning, I thought "What a beautiful day. Grey and cold." After breakfast we had a meeting of the War Cabinet. I can now remember all their names — my friend Chris, Douglas, of course, Norma Lamont, Mr King, and the man who sits at the end of the table who is some kind of lawyer.

Douglas began by saying that he wanted to tell us about his Peace Plan. I said: "Don't be silly, Douglas. Don't you know the war's still on." He went a bit red. Norma broke the silence by asking whether we'd heard the story about the three Iraqi soldiers and the Irish nurse. I said: "No, I don't think it was in the *Independent* this morning." They all laughed.

Monday

There was some really exciting news on the radio this morning. Apparently in South Africa, which I checked on my map is right down at the bottom of Africa, Mr de Klerk has abolished apartheid. This is really good news as it means that England can now play cricket in South Africa again.

The last time we played against South Africa, as all *Wisden*-lovers like myself know, was in 1968 when Pieter van der Kaffirbasher scored 157 not out in a third-wicket stand with Kepler van der Krugerrand, which was a record for a touring side at the Oval. I mentioned this to everyone at the meeting, and then casually asked if anyone knew what "apartheid" meant. Mr Waldegrave said it didn't matter now that it was all over, but just to remember that there was no longer any difference between black and white. My friend Chris chipped in: "You'll like it, John, it means everyone will be grey." Our meetings are very informal — oh yes — and have been so for quite some considerable period of time.

Tuesday

Snow! Who'd have thought it. I thought it was a good job I didn't have to go out to work, or I might never get there! Norman asked me whether I would like hot milk on my Weetabix. "Oh yes," I said. That shows how cold it is.

After breakfast there was a knock at the door. It was a man from Whitehall who asked whether I could explain the regulations for helping old people with their heating bills that I introduced in 1987. Those were the days when Mrs Thatcher was Prime Minister, and I had real power!

I said that it was very simple and I got out my calculator

to explain. I also got out the thermometer Norman and I bought in Torremolinos in 1983. It is a model of a bullfighter holding a cape, only his sword is actually a thermometer. "Look," I said. "First you have to wait till the temperature has gone down to minus 13°, or just past the bull's horns. When it has done that five days running, or seven days if there are only two in between when it hasn't been above minus 11°,

then any bona fide pensioner living on Social Security can fill in a simple four-page application with their birth certificate, and if the local benefit office adjudicates in their favour a sum of £3.75 will be sent to them or their surviving relatives."

When I had finished, I noticed that the man from Whitehall had fallen asleep. Perhaps, I thought, they are having to work too hard. It is not at all like that programme, *Oh Yes, Prime Minister.*

Wednesday

Sir Charles Powell, our Foreign Affairs adviser, came in to see me after the War Cabinet meeting and said that he was just going round to talk to Mrs Thatcher to tell her everything that had happened. As you can imagine, I got pretty cross about this. "You silly twit," I said to him. "You've got it completely wrong. You go to see Mrs Thatcher *before* our meetings, and then come back and brief me so that we know what to do."

When I told my friend Chris about this, I said: "Honestly, you wonder how some people get the job." "You certainly do," he replied, giving me one of his funny looks!

Thursday

We were all sitting around in the War Cabinet this morning, wondering when they were going to start the ground war (obviously we won't be told for security reasons), when suddenly there was a huge bang outside in the garden.

We looked out of the window, and there was a cloud of smoke going up from where my snowman used to be. All that was left was his grey scarf.

The silence was broken by Norma Lamont. "That's the best bang I've had for weeks," he said. Everybody laughed, but I wasn't quite sure why. I said to them all: "Don't worry, I expect it's only one of those Scud missiles." Then I looked at my map on the wall and I was very surprised to see that in fact we are much too far away from Iraq for one of their rockets to land on my garden. "Thank goodness for that," I said. "It's only the IRA."

Friday

Stopped at a Happy Eater on my way to Scarborough where I have to speak to some young people.

We have a very remarkable meal and I have kept the menu as a souvenir. This is what I had:

The Doncaster Slipway Happy Classless Sizzler
(one choice only due to adverse weather conditions)

Eggs, Sausage, Tomato, Bacon, Mushrooms *plus* HP Sauce

— ✳ —

Earl Grey Tea (my favourite)

— ✳ —

Toast, Marmalade

Sad to say, the service was a little slow and could do with improving. This gave me an idea for my speech: "Better services for all." It went down very well, oh yes — unlike my breakfast.

Monday

Today I had to go to Germany to meet the German Prime Minister who is called Mr Kohl. Mr Hurd told me that I should call him Herr, but I think it is a bit familiar to call him by his first name when I hardly know him.

When I got on the aeroplane I noticed that there were hundreds of people on it. Everyone's been saying that the airlines are having a rotten time because of the recession. What rubbish! My plane was remarkably full. It was a block booking of journalists who were all going to Germany like me. What a coincidence!

When I arrived I was taken in a car to see Mr Kohl, who lives in a big castle. I realised at once that we had a lot in common because his suit was exactly the same colour as mine, which broke the ice nicely.

After that we had to go into a big room. I saw all the people I had met on the plane coming over. It's a small world!

Tuesday

Today we had another meeting of the War Cabinet. The new steel shutters over the windows made the room a bit dark, but it meant we could see the television very well, to find out what we were doing in the Gulf. Apparently Mr Gorbachev is trying to spoil everything by having a peace proposal, but then Mr Bush rang up and left a message with my secretary to say that we weren't to take any notice of it, and I needn't even bother to read it. What a relief. Norma told us all rather a long story about something that had happened at Andrew Lloyd-Webber's wedding, which he had been to. It was all about him making "a proposal to some piece". I didn't really get the point, but everyone else laughed.

Wednesday

When I arrived at my desk this morning, Mr Heseltine was sitting behind it.

"Ah, John," he said, when I came in. "I've had a brilliant idea to help us win the next election."

He opened his briefcase and took out an envelope, on the back of which he had scribbled some notes.

"What is going to lose us the next election?" he said in a very important voice. "I'll tell you. The poll tax." "I know that perfectly well," I told him. "That's why I've put someone in charge of it."

Mr Heseltine then explained his new scheme for abolishing the poll tax and replacing it with a new tax based on how much people's houses are worth. "That means that the rich people will pay more than the poor people." "Gosh," I said, "that's absolutely brilliant, Michael. What shall we call it?"

"I've even thought of that," he said. "It is called the rates."

Thursday

Everyone is complaining that they can't get into work because of the IRA bombs. Only a few weeks ago they were complaining that they didn't have any work to go to. Honestly, you can't please some people whatever you do!

The BBC rang up wanting to know what my favourite records were. My friend Chris, who was in the room, suggested "record unemployment, record inflation, record bankruptcies". It is typical of Chris to be so flippant over what is a serious matter — i.e. what my favourite records are. I thought for a considerable period of time and said: " 'Oh Boy' by Buddy Holly and the Cricket, which is incidentally my favourite game."

Friday

This afternoon I had to go to the House of Commons for Question Time. I'm really beginning to get quite good at answering the questions. The first one today was from Mr Kinnock, who asked: "Would the Prime Minister not agree that the Government's policy on the Gulf is absolutely right?" He was obviously trying to catch me out by being much shorter than usual, and not giving me time to think. But I was more than a match for him. "Oh, yes," I said, and sat down.

Then Mr Ashdown asked his question. He has been in the army so you have to listen carefully. "Will the Prime Minister accept our assurances that we are right behind him in his determination to win this war?" Guess what I replied? "I refer you to the answer I made earlier to the Leader of the Opposition." That saw him off!

Saturday

Today I am having a party at Number Ten Downing Street, which is where I live. They said I could invite anyone I liked, so long as it included the Bulgarian prime minister. My friend Chris said I would easily recognise him because he would be the one wearing a grey suit and carrying a poisoned umbrella. I think he must have been joking again, because everyone was wearing a grey suit!

But the star guest was a girl called Kate

Bush. I spent a considerable period of time talking to her in the hopes that she might pass on some of the things that her father was planning to do in the Gulf War, but she pretended to know nothing about it. They are very well trained, these Americans.

Sunday

A momentous day. Mr Bush rang me up on the grey phone next to the bed. He said: "John Boy, we're kicking Iraqi ass." Obviously this is a secret code, which I spent some considerable period of time trying to work out. However, Mr Bush is no fool. The code does not feature in my 1965 *Look and Learn Secret Cypher Manual*. I go back to sleep and dream I am Smiley.

Monday

Amazing news. The ground war has started. I tell the War Cabinet that this is my own decision and that Mr Bush agreed with my proposals "to kick Iraqi ass". Mr Waldegrave, who I have to admit I do not hit it off with, says: "Well done, Prime Minister. I always said you could do this job in your sleep." If, peradventure, there is a Cabinet reshuffle, he may be spending considerably more time with his family.

We then turned on the television to watch what Mr Hurd had told us was going to be an important morale-boosting broadcast from the one woman who unites the nation in times of crisis. Imagine my surprise when the Queen came on. I wish the BBC would stop messing about with the programme.

March

Monday

At 6.30 this morning I was woken up by Mr Hurd. He handed me a plane ticket and told me that today was the day I had decided to go to Russia. "Oh, yes," I said, "I have seen it on the map in my office. It is a very big place. You could easily get lost." "That's a good idea!" said my friend Chris, who had just popped in to make sure that I had been briefed on what I was to say to Mr Gorbachev when I got there.

Mr Hurd told me that the Russians were going through a very difficult patch, because their economy is in ruins and they have very bad inflation. "That's good," I said, "it means we will have a lot in common."

The most important thing to decide was what I should wear, because Russia is very cold. Norman has bought me a grey fox-fur hat, which looks very stylish! It matches the suit I am going to wear. Mr Hurd has also given me a special phrase book of Russian words, compiled by the experts at the Foreign Office. The first one is "Mrs Thatcher is very well. Thank you for asking." The next one is "I am John Major. Our policies remain unchanged."

On the plane to Moscow I noticed a lot of journalists whom I had met in Germany. In my considered judgement it was very nice indeed to see them again! On the flight I practised my Russian and, by the time we landed, I had already learned to say "Oh da" which means "oh yes". Chris told me that this was all I needed to reply whenever Mr Gorbachev said something.

Tuesday

Here I am in Red Square. It is much bigger than you'd think from the pictures, but in other ways it is exactly like Streatham because the only shop is a McDonald's. They told me that Mr Gorbachev was free to see me and I was taken in to a very big room with chandeliers. There was Mr Gorbachev, just like in his pictures. He shook hands with me and then he began to make a speech which lasted a very considerable period of time. In fact, I looked at my watch and it took four hours. Then I thanked him for giving me so much of his time. Afterwards, I was taken into another room to talk to the journalists who had come with me on the plane. I told them that, in my judgement, Mr Gorbachev was a man I could do business with whom, which is what Mrs Thatcher used to say when she met him!

Then I had some free time for sightseeing. I suggested that I should meet the famous Mr Yeltsin, whom I had heard so much about, but they said that he was not important, and anyway he was probably drunk and would soon be dead. Instead, they suggested that I should go to the Tomb of the Unknown Soldier, but unfortunately the taxi driver said he didn't know where it was.

Wednesday

Today we went to Kuwait. To get there we had to go to Africa, India and lots of other countries which I had never been to before. I must remember to look them up on my map when I get home! I said to Mr O'Donnell that it would be very nice to be able to see things for myself and to travel incognito without anyone knowing who I was. He said he was sure that there wouldn't be any problem with this. And it was true. When we arrived, no one seemed to take any notice at all. He must have radioed ahead, oh yes.

When we were in the airport, I took off my fur hat and changed into a special grey pullover that Norman had put in for me to wear in the desert.

Then they said that they were going to take me for a drive, but that they couldn't tell me exactly where for security reasons. After we had been driving around for a very considerable period of distance, we came to lots of soldiers standing round a tank. A general with a French name who spoke very good English shouted: "Stand easy, gentlemen, there's someone here who wants to say a few words to you."

I got up on the tank and told them Norma's joke about the camel and the two Iraqi doctors. They all laughed, except me. I still don't understand it! Then I said I hoped they would all be home soon in time for the next election, but that of course I couldn't tell them the exact date when that would be. I began to explain to them why I couldn't say any more at this time, but I noticed that they were so tired after all the fighting that they had fallen asleep. Then the French general called for "three cheers for Tom King" and they all woke up.

Thursday

Today I got home to find Mr Heseltine sitting at my desk as usual. "Come in, John," he said, "I've got something very important to tell you." "Oh, yes," I said. "Have you decided what we're going to do about the poll tax?" "Yes," he said, "I've decided to leave it as it is until after the election." "But then we'll lose and I'll be out of a job," I said. "Dead right, squire," he said, putting his feet up on my desk, "you're not as dim as you look." "Thank you," I told him. We hit it off very well indeed nowadays. I used to think he didn't like me.

Friday

When I was having breakfast, imagine my surprise when I saw in the newspaper that there had been an opinion poll which said that I was the most popular prime minister there had ever been. Even more popular than Mr Churchill. I suppose there are some similarities. We have both won a war against a man with a moustache.

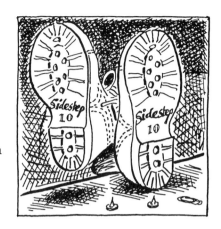

Saturday

Chris pops in to tell me the news about the by-election in somewhere called Ribble. I could not find it on my *Daily Telegraph* map so obviously it can't be very important.

"It's bad news," says Chris. "It was one of our safest seats." I thought about this for a considerable period of time and then I said: "Of course it will be quite different when it comes to the General Election." "It had better be," he said, "or we will be out of a job. And by the way have you heard what Mrs Thatcher said in America? It's no help having her sounding off in the background."

I had to disagree. "I wouldn't be where I was today if it wasn't for Mrs Thatcher, and her ideas are very helpful," I said.

Monday

I'm afraid I am in danger of becoming upset. More so than I have been for some considerable period of time. When Norman brought in the papers this morning while I was having breakfast, she showed me a number of items which she had marked with one of my special grey highlighters. "Look at what that woman has been saying," she said. "She obviously thinks she is still Prime Minister." And, sure enough, she was right. My wife, Norman, I mean, not Mrs Thatcher. Apparently, Mrs Thatcher has been going round telling the Americans that all the people who voted for me to become Prime Minister were "traitors" and "cowards", and that I have not been carrying out her policies. How hurtful, after all I have done. Norman says that I must not allow myself to be bossed about by a woman. "You are right, as always, my dear," I told her. From now on I am going to show Mrs Thatcher that my policies are totally different from hers, and when I think of them they jolly well will be.

Tuesday

I have decided to show everyone who is boss. I am going to see Herr Kohl. Mrs Thatcher never got on with him and she will really hate it when I am photographed smiling with him and calling him Helmut. This time I hope he will remember my name!

I caught the aeroplane in the morning and Mr Kohl fitted me in for a meeting in his office after lunch. Afterwards, I asked Mr O'Donnell, my pressman, how it had gone. He said everything had turned out just as we planned. He had told all the papers that my meeting had marked a historic departure. The dreadful divisive days of Thatcherism were over and a new era of mutual co-operation was ushering in a new dawn. Oh yes. All the journalists obviously agreed, because this was exactly what they wrote the next day. She will be very considerably cross indeed in my judgement! Ha, ha.

Wednesday

A funny thing about this job is that you never know which country you'll be in next. Mr Hurd came in this morning and said that President Bush was going on a golfing holiday in Bermuda, and that he might have time to fit in a quick meeting with me, if it was convenient. Mr Hurd said that it would be very useful if there could be some pictures in the papers of me and President Bush, to remind Mr Bush of how well he and I get on.

Thursday

Bermuda is much further away than you think. We seemed to be on the aeroplane for an awfully long time, and it was hard to sleep because they kept on showing films. When the plane landed Mr Bush had personally sent someone to fetch me to his golf course. When I arrived he said: "John, boy, you're looking terribly grey around the gills." "Thank you, Mr President," I replied. "I bet some guy keeps ringing you up in the middle of the night telling you what to do," he said. How did he know? He is certainly a very extraordinary man. No wonder he won the war.

Friday

Apparently I am very ill. All the papers are saying it, so perhaps they are right. When we had our daily Cabinet meeting, my friend Chris said: "You look Bushed." I laughed, as it was obviously meant to be one of his jokes! But I did admit that I had a bit of a sore throat. Then Norma Lamont winked at everyone and said: "You'd better go and suck a Fisherman's Friend." Everybody sniggered, but I said that, in fact, I had some Strepsils, which are very considerably more effective in my experience.

I then announced that I had decided to scrap the Poll Tax. (This caused some surprise because I always used to refer to it as the community charge!) "This is a very brave move," I said.

"Yes, John," said Chris. "Getting rid of the most unpopular tax in history certainly takes guts."

After lunch my wife, Norman, said that she needed my study for an hour, as she had to talk to someone from our local paper in Huntingdon. After I had agreed, the doorbell rang and a very fierce-looking young lady came in and pushed past me. Norman said over her shoulder: "The one with the glasses is my husband," as they disappeared into the study.

Saturday

"Look," said Norman, as she brought me the papers. "I've got you a scoop." I looked at the headlines. "PM AT DEATH'S DOOR", said one. "MY JOHN IS TOO ILL TO DO THE JOB SAYS NORMA", said another. "Why on earth did you tell them that?" I asked her. "I wanted to show them that you were not like Mrs Thatcher," she said, with a proud smile. "No one ever said that she was ill."

Monday

Norman is very busy nowadays giving interviews to the press. This leaves her considerably less periods of time to cook my supper. Tonight, for example, I had yesterday's leftovers — i.e. a plate of mashed potatoes. As I was eating them, however, I had one of my ideas, oh yes, which I wrote down immediately on the back of Norman's message ("Your dinner is in the fridge"). It struck me that the mashed potatoes were, in my judgement, very similar to the policies of the Labour Party! I shall make this the climax of my pre-election speech in Southport. (Note: Must ask Chris if we *are* having the election.)

Tuesday

Budget Day! I always enjoy The Budget because of the long and detailed speeches about fiscal policy. It is nearly as much fun to listen to as to present, as I told Norma Lamont since it was his turn this year.

He told a joke about mobile phones, which was the first of his jokes I have ever understood. No one laughed though, perhaps because he put up a tax called VAT. In the old days Mrs Thatcher used to cut taxes, which shows how different things are nowadays.

The Labour Party, no doubt annoyed by my "mashed potatoes" idea, have described me as "a gutless corporate creep". I object strongly to this. To call me corporate when we all agreed in Cabinet that I was my own man just makes them look silly.

Anyway, as David Mellor, who's becoming a very good friend of mine, said: "Look at it this way, Prime Minister. They were never this rude about Mrs Thatcher. You must be very different indeed." Oh yes.

Monday

Today I woke up early as it is a very special day. They have kindly asked me to go to Madame Tussauds to see the new waxwork they have done of the Prime Minister — who, of course, is me now! It is quite strange walking into a room and seeing yourself standing there, absolutely life-like! They even remembered the biro in my top pocket!

As I was standing there next to the model some schoolboys came past and one of them said to the teacher: "Sir, which one of those is the dummy?" The teacher said that, as far as he was concerned, they both were. "But look over there, boys," he said, "there's someone really interesting." Imagine my surprise when I saw he was pointing at Mrs Thatcher. I thought they always melted down the old one. But the man who was showing me round, Mr Tussaud, explained that sometimes they had to keep the old ones in case they came back.

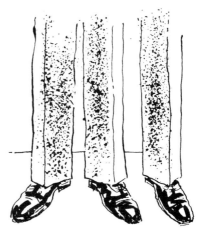

Tuesday

Now that there is peace in the Middle East I have got time to do lots of things that I have been putting off. For instance, today I went to the races with Norman. Mr O'Donnell said that the papers would like it, because it would show that I knew how to relax, unlike some people who have been in 10 Downing Street during the past eleven years I could mention! For my day out I wore my racing outfit, a grey suit with matching tie.

When it was time for the first race, everyone said: "I suppose, Prime Minister, you're going to back the grey?" They all laughed. "Oh no," I said. "I shall, after a considerable period of due consideration, place a prudent bet on the horse which in my judgement is most likely to prove the winner." Unfortunately it came last.

Wednesday

Something I have always wanted to be is the castaway on the famous programme *Desert Island Discs*. So imagine my delight when Mr O'Donnell said that Sue Lawley had invited me on to her show.

I have always known what records I would choose, so I only had to decide on a book (apart from the Bible and Shakespeare) and a luxury item. This did not take me a considerable period of time to work out, because I am not, as many people have said, a ditherer. Oh no. I can be very decisive when I want to be! My book would be the new 1991 *Wisden*, although I am not sure about my luxury. So I asked my friend Chris, who said: "I know. You should take a pocket calculator. Then you can work out the new poll tax!"

Unfortunately, when Miss Lawley arrived it turned out that there had been a mistake. It wasn't *Desert Island Discs* at all. She only wanted to interview me, which was quite a disappointment.

Sue is certainly a very good-looking lady, as Norma Lamont had warned me! She began by asking me whether I had any 'O' levels. "Oh yes," I said. "I think I definitely might have had a considerable number to be precise." You have to watch these women interviewers closely, as Norma Lamont had advised me with one of his winks. Then she asked me whether I minded that everyone thought that I was very grey and boring. "Well," I said, "everyone is entitled to his or her own point of view in matters of this kind. We are fortunate enough to live in a democratic society, where people must come to their own judgement on a wide variety of issues, and I would certainly defend everyone's right so to do." That put her in her place! Indeed she had sunk down in her armchair, looking quite dazed by the force of my reply!

Her last question was whether being Prime Minister had made a difference to my life. "Oh yes," I said. "In the old days Norman and I could go down to the local Gateway supermarket and no one would know who we were. Now everybody stops and points and says, 'Oh look, there's that Mrs Major, who's always giving those interviews saying that her husband won't last much longer.'"

April

Thursday

Mr Hurd rang up early this morning to say that he was just off to see his Chinese friend, Mr Dung (this always makes my friend David Mellor laugh at our Cabinet meetings). Mr Hurd said that we might be in a bit of trouble because of the Kurds. When he rang off I looked on my map but I couldn't see them marked anywhere, so they can't be that important! I am glad to say that Mr Bush agrees with me about this one. He very kindly rang me up in the middle of the night to say that he couldn't interfere in the affairs of another country and nor could Britain. Could I pass this on to whoever was in charge?

Friday

Well, really! My patience is beginning to wear considerably thin. When I opened the paper this morning, there was Mrs Thatcher telling everyone that we should be helping the Kurds in their hour of need. As a mother and grandmother, she said it was her duty to speak out. Honestly, this is interference in the internal affairs of another country, i.e. Britain! One of these days I'm going to have to ask President Bush to tell her who's boss.

Saturday

I have decided to send a certain amount of financial aid to the Kurds who I have discovered live in lots of different countries but not Iraq any more. This is nothing to do with Mrs Thatcher at all. It is a decision of my own making which I made at a football match whilst Mrs Thatcher was on the television. I shall make this point to Radio One's Steve Wright who, Mr O'Donnell tells me, is a top-notch political interviewer with a very big following amongst classless young people. He is certainly more popular than Jimmy Young (a friend of guess who!) who everyone now thinks is a grey-haired old bore. I said this to Chris who laughed in a funny way.

Monday

I really am beginning to get very considerably annoyed by Mrs Thatcher. She has been in America again, telling everyone that my government is a "B team". Well, all I can say is who appointed all of us in the first place? Oh yes, she has a lot to answer for! This is the kind of thing that I will have to say to her when we have our big show-down, which will be when a suitable moment arises. She is not the only one who is being rude about me in front of my back. The Young Conservatives are saying that I am a ditherer and that I cannot make up my mind about anything. It is very hard to know what to reply.

Tuesday

Who are this Bruges Group who are in the papers criticising me? I have looked up Bruges on my map and it is in Belgium, which is nowhere near Iraq, let alone Oxford, which is where they all seem to come from. Mr Hurd tells me that it is run by a man called Professor Norma Stone, which only goes to prove what I said to Sue Lawley, or was it that very funny DJ on Radio One — that just because you are a professor and have passed a lot of exams, it doesn't mean to say you know anything. Anyway, they say Mr Bush and I are not doing anything about the Kurds. How do they know this? It was meant to be top-secret.

Wednesday

I have had a brilliant idea in the middle of the night. We must do something about the Kurds! I told my wife Norman my brilliant idea at breakfast time. "But what will you do?" she asked. How typical of a woman to pour cold water and nitpick. I told her that it was for other people to work out the details. The prime minister's job is to have the Grand Vision, like Mrs Thatcher used to do. After breakfast we had a Cabinet meeting when I announced my brilliant bombshell. They were so stunned that they all sat silently for a considerable period of seconds. Then Chris said, "That's all very brilliant, John, but what can we do?"

"Honestly, Chris, you're worse than my wife," I said. "I've done the hard work — surely you lot, with all your O-levels, can work out some safe place for them to go to." I can be pretty fierce when I choose to be! So they all put their heads together and came up with the idea that all the Kurds should go to Iraq which is where they used to live before we won the war, but only in places where they would be safe. These would be called "safe havens", which funnily enough was the name of my first bank manager's house in Haywards Heath (Mr Kimbolton).

I was so excited that after the meeting I rang up President Bush on the special phone we have. Unfortunately, it was in the middle of the night in America, and he was asleep, so I left my plan about the safe havens on his answering machine.

When I had gone to sleep that night Mr Bush returned my call to say that it wasn't my job to go round having ideas, and he would let me know if and when we needed to do anything about the Kurds. Sometimes he can be almost as fierce as I can!

Thursday

This morning we had another Cabinet meeting, and to my surprise no one mentioned my idea about the Kurds. Instead Norma Lamont said that if we wanted to win the next election, easily the best votewinner would be a new act to give more freedom for landlords to evict unsuitable tenants.

I listened to what Norma had to say with considerable interest, but for some reason all the others began to titter. Eventually my friend Chris said: "Stop dominating the meeting, Norma." "Correction," said David Mellor, amid the laughter. At this Norma got very red in the face and said it was no laughing matter what some poor landlords had to put up with these days. He explained that a good friend of his had got a tart in the basement and there was nothing he could do. I was about to tell him that his friend should put it in the pantry but Chris interrupted: "I suppose you'll be demanding a three-line whip on this one," he said with a snigger. I had no idea what they were all on about. I am not surprised that some people call them the B team! "Gentlemen!" I said, calling them to order. "Can we get back to something really important, like the poll tax?" Everyone yawned, except Mr Heseltine, who began to give us his proposals for replacing the community charge. "I've got a complete package of preferred options fully worked out," he said, producing an old envelope with lots of small writing on it in pencil. "However, I am not yet at liberty to reveal what they are, at this moment in time." "Oh yes you are, Michael," said Chris, as he seized the envelope, and announced: "Gentlemen, we are apparently to replace the poll tax with chocolates for wife, take suit to cleaners and hair gel."

Friday

Today I had a very exciting trip to Birmingham, where they were having a special exhibition called "Business Communication Tools '91". When I got there they gave me a special pen-holder with three biros in the shape of cricket stumps. Someone must have told them that I was interested in cricket. And biros! Mr O'Donnell had decided that I should be photographed holding one of the new Vodacell PX177T phones, which has a range of over 3,000 miles. This was fortunate as at that very moment in time the phone began to ring, and guess who it was — Mr Bush from Washington. He said: "John boy, I've

had a great idea about the Kurds. We're gonna find somewhere where these people can be truly safe. We've even gotta
name — 'safe havens'. Pretty good, huh? I know I'm going to
have your full support on this one, John baby. Enjoy." To be
considerably honest, I did not enjoy the rest of my day in the
smallest degree.

Monday

I am still to a significant degree annoyed with people going
on about my 'O' levels. What could be less relevant and more
snobbish than going on and on about someone's 'O' levels?
Norman is being very supportive about this and I overheard
her on the telephone telling the newspapers to stop all the 'O'
level stuff. "You're making him ill," she said. "He won't last
much longer if you carry on like this."

Later a very pleasant and agreeable doctor came round,
who told me that on the contrary I was looking very well. He
is a quite exceptionally perceptive man (called Owen or
something similar) and he said that he admired everything I
had done.

I immediately offered him a job. The doctor, David, said he
would think about it but when I told my friend Chris about
this he was amazed.

"Did you ask him to examine your head?" he asked.

On occasion Chris can be quite dense. Sometimes I wonder
how he got any 'O' levels at all.

May

Monday

I cannot understand why people are complaining that Mr
Heseltine's new council tax is too complicated. As I joked to
Norman over breakfast this morning: "You hardly need six 'O'
Levels in Maths to understand it! You simply assess which of
the fourteen bands your house comes into and then work out
that if you've only got an average of 1.3 persons living in the
property in question, then your council tax liability will fall
within the government guidelines!" How anyone can say this
is complicated, when Mr Heseltine originally wanted to have
34 bands, is beyond me. Thanks to my decisive intervention
at our Cabinet meeting last week, the whole thing is now so

simple that I am sure we will win the local elections hands down!

Tuesday

I woke up this morning feeling that a great weight has been taken off my mind. Now that the poll tax is dead and buried, all our problems are as good as over.

Mind you, some people are never satisfied. I read in the paper this morning that a lot of businessmen at a meeting somewhere have been complaining about the economy and saying that things are getting worse. What a considerable load of rubbish this is. At our Cabinet meeting this morning, Norma Lamont told us all that everything was going to be all right and that the recovery was only just around the corner. I for one was very reassured to hear this, because after all he *is* the Chancellor of the Exchequer, so he should know! Oh yes. I used to say the same thing when I was the Chancellor of the Exchequer, and people always believed me.

My friend Chris then said to Norma: "So what you mean is that there is a red light at the end of the tunnel." Everyone laughed at this, which shows that they must all be pretty confident that everything is going to be all right.

Wednesday

I am getting very considerably annoyed by what is happening about the Kurds. I was looking at my wall map this morning, which now has a large pin at the top with a paper flag marked "Safe Haven". My wife Norman typed this out for me so that it looks really professional. This shows that I have done my bit to solve the problem, but where, oh where is the flag saying "United Nations Kurdkeeping Force"? Where are the troops of Finland, Ireland and the Gabon? Where is the Zairian Navy that Mr Hurd promised me would soon be on its way to the mountains?

Honestly, if you don't do it yourself, nothing gets done in this world! No wonder Norman has told *Hello!* that I am at death's door! I have decided to write a very stiff letter indeed to Mr de Kwelluar *(check spelling with Mr Waldegrave — I do not recall getting an 'O' Level in this subject!)*. He is the man in charge of the United Nations, and I shall tell him in no uncertain terms to pull out all his fingers on this one. Also, it will show the world how tough I am when my letter is published in all tomorrow's papers, under Mr O'Donnell's suggested heading NOW MAJOR GETS TOUGH WITH UN.

Thursday

Today something really important has happened. I have had a letter telling me that I have been elected as a member of the MCC. Usually you have to wait a very considerable period of years (18) to get in. I however have been allowed to join immediately. This is definite proof that Britain is becoming a classless society, when someone from my background can

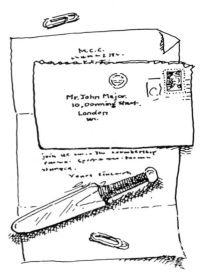

join such an elitist club without having to wait, a club that includes such famous names as Jeffrey Archer and Tim Rice.

Furthermore, it might be pointed out, this particular honour is one that was never granted to Mrs Thatcher in all the eleven years that she was Prime Minister. It must make her very bitter.

Friday

While I was talking to my friend Chris this morning about the Benson & Hedges first round, Mr Baker came in to say that he hoped I didn't mind, but there was a major constitutional crisis.

Apparently it is something to do with the War Crimes Bill. I thought we had all forgotten about this one. Oh no, said Mr Baker, who has a considerably annoying smile. We owe it to Mrs Thatcher, he said. This was her baby and we should make sure that the bill was passed to show that we haven't rejected absolutely everything she stood for.

I said that in my personal judgement it would be a remarkable mistake to pass this bill, as it could not work and it would get us all into a by no means small mess.

My friend Chris said: "It will be a fitting memorial to Mrs Thatcher, then." But Mr Baker did not smile.

Saturday

People are complaining that we have done badly in the local elections. What rubbish! When you sit down and look at the figures with considerable consideration you can see that we could have done much worse. We could have lost all the seats. That would have warranted some criticism but a mere 800 lost is hardly something to write home about. Anyway, as Chris says, "Now we don't have to have a June election."

This is a weight off my mind as I will now be able to go to the Test Matches in peace and sit in the pavilion.

"That's one seat you haven't lost," said Mr Waldegrave, who I must admit is not my flavour of the month.

His handling of the National Health issue has been quite feeble. "It is not my job to run the National Health Service"(!) he said. For a supposedly clever man who has been to Oxford Mr Waldegrave (pronounced 'Wargrave' as he always insists) is pretty dense. I said to Chris: "It is like me saying 'It is not my job to run the country.'" Chris gave me one of his funny looks.

Sunday

Mr Bush has had heart troubles and I have sent him a Get Well Soon card which Norman chose in W.H. Smith. It shows a man playing golf with the message "In the rough? Hope you are back on the fairway soon."

However, I can't help thinking that it serves Mr Bush right. After all, only a few weeks ago he was telling me that *I* looked ill, which everyone used as an excuse to be rude about me. Well, who is looking terrible now?

Monday

Mr O'Donnell tells me that I have been very considerably enjoying a television programme called *The Darling Buds of May*. When I asked him what he was talking about he said that he had already told the papers that it was my favourite programme, which showed how in touch I was with the way the millions of ordinary classless people think. He gave me a video that he had sent for from the television company. Norman and I watched it whilst we were eating our lunch. I was in no small measure appalled. It was about a man who didn't pay his taxes. As I said to Norman, if everyone behaved like this man in the programme the country would be in a complete mess, with unemployment soaring, the government having to borrow billions of pounds and the economy collapsing about our ears. I rang Mr O'Donnell and told him what I thought of his video, but he said it didn't matter at all. "I've already worked it into your Perth speech," he said, "where you promise at the end that everything in this country will soon be 'considerably perfick'."

Tuesday

Today is the day of my big policy speech in Perth. I looked it up on the map in my office and discovered that it is a place in Australia, but fortunately Mr Hurd came in and saved me from a considerably long journey because, in fact, I had to go to Scotland! "Well, that is just perfick," I said, hoping to raise a smile from Mr Hurd, but he only replied, "The word is 'perfect', John, please don't embarrass us in public."

In fact my speech went down very well. I said: "I know you are all expecting a very important announcement from me. Well, here it is. I'm certainly not going to announce anything important today!" I got a standing ovation for this.

Wednesday

I had put aside this evening for sticking in my collection of Famous Cricketer cigarette cards. The problem is whether to put them in alphabetical or batting order. E.g. Should C.L. Badcock be ahead of Cyril Washbrook, or vice versa? In my judgement there are merits to both cases. I cannot decide. But my old friend Jeffrey Archer solved the problem for me when he rang up to say it was very important for me to spend that evening at a concert at Wembley. I told him I had something even more important to do, but he said that the next election could easily depend on my being there. The concert  was to raise money for the Kurds and everyone was going to be there, including Mr Kinnock and Mr Ashdown. I pointed out that I had already met them. No, said Jeffrey, the point is it is vital for you to be associated with good causes, rather than just the Conservative Party.

Thursday

My enthusiasm for Europe is very markedly on the wane. When I was the Chancellor of the Exchequer there was a great fuss about only having one sort of money in Europe. I remember my friend Chris joked at the time that this was to be called the Deutschmark, but in fact it was called the Ecu. Mrs Thatcher didn't want this at all, so I came up with what everyone agreed was a brilliant compromise which I called the Hard Ecu, an expression which soon caught on to a very appreciable degree.

My proposal was very simple. Everyone would have the choice, if he was paying for a meal in a restaurant, for example, to pay either in my new Hard Ecus, or in whatever the local currency happened to be in the country in question, such as Belgian francs, pesetas or whatever. All that was needed was for commercial premises to convert all pricing to a dual system, altered daily according to the exchange rate measured against a basket of European currencies. Were you, for instance, to purchase three onions in Madrid, you could either pay 20 pesetas, or 1.3856 Hard Ecus, a simple enough sum you would have thought for the average shopkeeper. But oh no, say the grey men of Brussels! They have decided that one currency is much simpler. No wonder Mrs Thatcher got so remarkably cross with them all just before she resigned.

Friday

The Health Service is certainly giving me a headache! I have had to agree to meet the British Medical Association. At breakfast this morning I mentioned to Norman that I was seeing a lot of doctors later in the morning. Her eyes lit up and she rushed off to telephone her friend on *Hello!* magazine. I heard her say: "He's really bad this time. I think he's slipping away."

Later there was a knock at the door of my study, and the deputation came in, led by a very large man called Dr Paisley. As soon as he came in he banged his fist on my desk sending all the biros flying, and said that he was "very angry indeed" at the way the talks were going. He and his colleagues weren't going to stand for it any longer. I said to them that I could not be bullied, and that they should be grateful that

built more hospitals in the last ten years than any previous administration. This certainly shut the doctor up. He went purple in the face and stormed out, shouting: "This means war. It's your funeral, Major!" Norman must have heard this, because I later saw her telling her friend from *Hello* that the doctors had told me I was a terminal case.

Saturday

We have lost at the Monmouth By-Election by a quite considerable margin. Mr Waldegrave says that the Labour Party has been telling lies about the National Health. "That's our job," said my friend Chris. Mr Waldegrave said Labour told everyone that the local hospital was going to opt out. Given the result, I think it is perhaps time that Mr Waldegrave opted out as well.

Obviously what is now needed is a strong man at the top, a man who will spell out exactly what we mean. "Is Mrs Thatcher coming back then?" asked Mr Waldegrave. There are many job losses in the National Health Service and one more will not be noticed. Oh yes. Or rather, oh no.

Mrs Thatcher never even used the Health Service. She always went private whereas when Norman insisted that I have a check-up to make sure I'm still alive I joined the queue like everyone else. By the time they got to see me I was feeling 100 per cent better so I saved them the trouble.

Sunday

Well, the Labour Party are certainly on the run. All they can do is accuse us of "whingeing" about losing the by-election. What a pathetic charge to make! It is terribly unfair to accuse us of "whingeing". Where is one example of "whingeing" I would like to know or one example of us being bad losers? You see. We simply are not whingeing. Not at all. We're not. I cannot say this too often.

Monday

I wish someone would explain to me why the opinion polls are so gloomy. There was another one this morning which said that Labour is now 10 points ahead. When I was reading it at breakfast time, I said to my wife Norman: "These polls really make me sick." She immediately disappeared into the passage outside, where I heard her ringing up her friend on the *Hello!* magazine to say that "even John is now admitting that he is seriously ill".

But then, when I had got to my desk, Mr Baker came in and said: "It's all right, Prime Minister, I've found a sure way to win the next election."

"Oh yes?" I said, not entirely convinced, letting him know that he was not exactly my favourite person in the Cabinet. "And what might that be?"

"What is the most important issue in Britain today?" "Oh, that's easy," I said. "You don't need an O-level Economics degree to answer that one. Inflation, isn't it?" "No," he said, giving me one of his considerably annoying smiles. "It is the killer dogs which are rampaging through Britain — look at the front page of the *Sun*."

He held up a copy of that paper, which had a big headline saying PAGE 3 GIRL DIES OF CANCER. Below it was a picture of a snarling dog with the headline MAJOR MUST KILL THESE DOGS NOW.

Mr Baker looked triumphant as he said: "My plan is quite simple. You should kill these dogs now."

I hate to say it, but even Kenneth sometimes has quite good ideas. If I kill all the dogs it will make me very popular and will show people that I can act decisively when I want to. Mrs Thatcher never had the courage to shoot 10,000 dogs in a day.

Tuesday

What a relief! I have been told that the best thing I could do to help the country is to have a day off! Mr O'Donnell has rung the papers to say that I will be at Lord's watching cricket. Unfortunately, as I took my seat in the pavilion there was a slight misunderstanding, as one of the stewards said: "You can't sit there, sir, it's reserved for the Prime Minister." I explained that I was a guest of Mr Jeffrey Archer. This improved matters very considerably, and I was allowed to take my seat.

All interest was focused on the return of Ian Botham, who everyone had written off as an unpopular has-been. But I took very considerable comfort in the fact that he did so brilliantly, which I regarded as a good omen for my own comeback at the next election. Oh yes! Unfortunately at the end of the day he fell over and had to be carried off.

Wednesday

The Labour Party must be really desperate! They have hired a lady called Mrs Follett to tell them what colour suits to wear when they appear on television. It is all to do with whether you are a spring, summer or autumn person. Mr Kinnock is apparently a spring person, which is why he always wears a blue suit, whereas Mr Hattersley is autumn, which is why he wears brown. I must be a summer person, because all my suits are grey. What is more, I don't need some woman to tell me what to wear. Norman just puts it out on my bed in the morning.

Thursday

Mr Baker tells me there is a snag to my dog plan. Apparently it is very hard to catch the dogs in order to kill them, so perhaps my idea is not so good after all.

Hardly a day goes past when I am not to some degree annoyed by the latest antics of my predecessor. While I am busy at the cricket, she deliberately goes round the world getting herself on television by meeting world leaders. Yesterday it was President de Klerk, today it is Mr Gorbachev in Russia. When I showed the picture to the Cabinet, my friend Chris said: "If you're lucky, John, she might even want to come and meet *you.*" I told him that this was not the point.

The paper said that she had told the Russian voters it would be a terrible mistake to drop a leader who had been in power for so many years and achieved so much, in order to pick some untried nonentity. All the Cabinet laughed when I read this out, which only goes to show what a figure of fun she has become!

Friday

Mr Rifkind came in and told me in his Scottish accent that he had another idea which could win us the next election. Everyone should be encouraged to use the railways instead of the road. At first I couldn't

PARTY WORN

see the point of this, but then he went on to explain that his plan would, of course, make a very considerable change in the policy of the Government for the past twelve years.

"Mrs Thatcher would not have approved of my plan at all," he said. "She hated trains." I suddenly began to realise that my friend Malcolm was really on to something.

After lunch I told Chris that we had another election-winner up our sleeve.

"Not your bloody dogs again," he said, displaying what in my judgement was a marked lack of respect for my position as his boss. "No," I said, very decisively. "The dogs issue can be considered dead and buried." "More than can be said for the dogs," said Chris, slapping me on the back and causing one of my biros to fall out of my breast pocket onto the carpet, leaving a red mark which will not best please Norman. I tried to ignore him, explaining that my new plan for reviving British Rail would show once and for all just how totally different I am from Mrs Thatcher.

"Yes, she never lost an election," said Chris. If he is not careful, he may find himself joining Mr Waldegrave in my little grey book!

Sunday

My patience has been remarkably stretched by the news in the papers that Mrs Thatcher is telling all her friends that I was the wrong choice for the job. She said I am a grey man with no ideas. What on earth can one reply to that?

This shows once again that my predecessor has lost her grip. Let us follow the logic of her thinking. If you go into Waitrose and buy baked beans, the choice of brand is up to you. When you get to the checkout, you cannot suddenly blame the baked beans for being the wrong sort. Mrs Thatcher chose me and if I am the wrong choice then she is clearly to blame. Therefore she was lacking in judgement and had to be replaced. As I often say, QED!

June

Monday

I woke up this morning with a brilliant idea for winning the next election. It is called The Citizen's Charter. Like all great ideas it is very, very simple. Every citizen should have the right to get considerably angry with any public amenity which fails to provide a proper service. For instance, a commuter is waiting at a station, let us say Haywards Heath, for the 7.35 to take him to Victoria. He has a meeting with an important overseas buyer at 9.30. The train is 17 minutes late, owing to leaves on the line. The result is that he is late for the meeting, and a vital export order is thereby lost. As things stand at present,  the citizen has no redress in such circumstances. But under my new Charter, he will have the right to sue British Rail for compensation.

When I told my wife Norman about my idea, she was very enthusiastic. She at once thought of another application for the Charter. "What happens if you get held up in a traffic jam on the motorway?" she said. "Will you be able to sue all the other motorists who are in front of you?" She told me that this very circumstance had arisen last week, when she was on the way to a lunch given by *Hello!* magazine. "I was so late", she said, "that they weren't able to put in my story about how you keep me awake all night by covering the bed with those silly red boxes. I had to give it to the *Mail on Sunday* instead."

Tuesday

I am getting very considerably annoyed again by the way my predecessor keeps on telling foreign newspapers that I am not doing a good job as prime minister. This morning Mr O'Donnell brought in a copy of *Sumo Sushi*, the well-known Japanese paper for the raw fish industry, which had a big headline in Japanese saying, "Phew What A Thatcher: Iron Maiden Calls For Return To Poll Tax". How silly can you get?! If I was to bring back the poll tax, Labour would shoot ahead on the polls, and we might be in very considerable danger of losing the next election! You obviously don't have to be very bright to be prime minister, I thought when I read her interview.

Wednesday

I've had another brilliant idea for my Charter. One of the real menaces of the modern world is when you have a ball-point pen in your pocket and it starts to leak, marking your shirt and suit and sometimes your vest, if it is winter-time. Under my Charter, you would be entitled to recover the cost of the dry-cleaning from the manufacturers. This is the kind of thing which will show the country that the Conservative Party under my leadership has got the real vision that is required for the 1990s. Oh yes, Mrs Thatcher would never have thought of this.

Thursday

All the papers are saying this morning that I cannot make up my mind over Europe. On the contrary, I have always made my position precisely clear. We should wait and see what happens, and then decide what to do. What could be clearer than that?

And another thing I have decided very decisively. Today I am going to watch the Test Match at Leeds. As I said to my friend Chris, "I am sure it will be worth watching, even though the West Indies, like the Conservatives, always win."

Friday

Great news. England won the Test! At the Cabinet meeting this morning I told *my* team that today I was going to finish off my number one opponent once and for all. "But she's in Japan," said Norma Lamont. "Oh no," I explained, "I mean Mr Kinnock." Mr Lamont was tired because he had just come back from a very important meeting in Brussels. He passed round some special balloons he had bought in Belgium, marked "For Union In Europe. Let's Keep It Safe". Everyone laughed, especially when Chris said that "it might help the HARD ECU". I was glad to see that not everyone had forgotten my idea of the "parallel currency" which I have explained in this diary before.

Later in the day, in the House of Commons, I made the toughest speech I have ever made, about the danger of the Labour Party winning the next election. I didn't pull any punches. "If that lot of people get in", I said, pointing in no uncertain terms to the empty bench opposite where Mr Kinnock and his friends usually sit, "the country will really be in a not inconsiderable mess." All our side cheered, even Mr Ridley, who shook his fist at me enthusiastically.

Saturday

Today is the Queen's birthday and Norman and I went to see the

Trooping of the Colour. It is a very traditional spectacle which I in no small measure enjoyed. It is also the day when the Birthday Honours are announced. This was the chance for me to show that the John Major style is very different from that of his predecessor. I chose:

1.   Cyril Washbrook whose autograph I still have in my album from the day in 1957 when he scored 33 not out against Surrey at the Oval. It says "Good Luck Brian from Cyril". Brian, I should explain, was a boy at school. I swapped it with him in exchange for a set of mint-condition Cape of Good Hope triangular stamps.

2.   Chris Barber. We all used to listen to his jazz music in the bank. "This will really appeal to young people," I said to my friend Chris. "Especially to all those over fifty," he said.

3.   Brian Clough. He was never in charge of England. "Just like you," said Mr Waldegrave. He now has four stars against his name in the little grey book. Oh yes.

These honours are symbolic of what I must modestly record they are now calling Majorism. Norman read this in the papers and said, "What does it mean?" I replied: "Isn't it obvious? Majorism. It means 'Major' plus 'ism'." Honestly, sometimes people can be very slow to catch on to new ideas.

Sunday

I cannot believe it! Mr O'Donnell has brought in a copy of the *Katmandu Courier*, of which the main headline was "Iron Lady Lashes 'Feeble' Major Over Europe". I ignored this completely, but immediately thought up another clause for my Charter, which I keep in a special ring-pull folder which Norman bought me for Christmas. It has a yellow cover, marked "Good Ideas!" This clause would be for people who take a new job, such as a senior managerial post, and who then find that their predecessor continually makes trouble for them. They would be entitled to full compensation for their hurt feelings and loss of reputation.

Monday

My wife Norman is most pleased. She has been invited to go to the opera to see *Tosca*, which is an opera. I asked her what it was about, and she said that it was a very sad story of a poor woman who ended up jumping out of a window to her death. Oh yes, I said, I can think of at least one woman who should take this option. Mr O'Donnell tells me that Mrs Thatcher is going to make one of her speeches, but she has promised that she will not rock the boat by saying how bad I am as a prime minister. I think I am beginning to get her under control, and that she will toe the line from now on.

Tuesday

I have read Mrs Thatcher's speech to the New Dworkin Prayer Breakfast Investment Club very carefully, and I was very very pleased to see she said that I was doing a "very good job" as Prime Minister. It was perhaps a pity, however, that she added, "apart from the fact that he is totally wrong about Europe." What I would like to know is how I could be wrong about Europe, when I haven't even made up my mind yet about what I am going to do! I am beginning to think that the Americans are rather wasting their money giving her £30,000 to make all these after-dinner speeches. They could do much better to get my friend Jeffrey Archer to do it. He will do it for nothing, so long as he can bring along some of his books to sign.

Wednesday

I was very pleased to see this morning that Mr Heath has come out very strongly on my side in the great debate. I will admit that in the past he was wrong to criticise Mrs Thatcher. But, as I told my friend Chris, I now realise that Mr Heath is only doing his duty by speaking out on the most important issue confronting this country today. "You mean, how to shut Mrs Thatcher up," said Chris. "No," I said very firmly, "I mean closer European union. This is in no way a debate about personalities at all." "Though I must admit", I went on, "that I was considerably struck by Mr Heath's reference to Mrs Thatcher's brain being 'minute'. Many people might think this was rude, but I am of the opinion that if you were actually to subject Mrs Thatcher's brain to close examination, you might well find that it was considerably smaller than that of certain people who might have many fewer academic qualifications."

Thursday

One of the things I most enjoy about the job of being prime minister is the number of times you have to go to Lord's in order to be seen on television. As always I took a scorebook, a new set of biros, a copy of *Wisden* and, on this occasion, my famous file containing the ideas for my Citizen's Charter. When rain stopped play with England on 25 for 7, I thought wouldn't it be a good idea if people whose sandwiches got wet at a cricket match could claim compensation for that proportion of their lunch which was rendered inedible by adverse weather conditions? For instance, a smoked salmon sandwich would command a higher rate of compensation than a Marmite sandwich, of the type Norman had prepared for me. After lunch, I had to go back to the House of Commons to answer questions. Mr McGregor warned me that the Labour people were going to set a trap for me by asking whether I disapproved of the fact that top businessmen were giving themselves huge pay rises. I devoted a considerable period of minutes working out a brilliant answer to this one. Sure enough, up got Mr Hattersley, huffing and puffing as usual, and asked: "Does the Prime Minister disapprove of top businessmen giving themselves huge pay rises?" Quick as a flash I jumped up, holding the ring-pull folder with all my answers, and said: "Oh yes, sir." Then I sat down. Everyone laughed and cheered at my brilliant reply, except Mr Hattersley who said: "Well, are you going to do anything about it?" I was not expecting this, but I came up with an answer just like that — "Oh no."

July

Friday

Today we had our big debate on Europe. I had been quite worried about this in case guess-who tried to ruin it all. But you can imagine how pleased I was when she gave a solemn assurance to Mr David Frost on his very popular programme *Sky At Night* that she was in no way going to rock the boat. In fact she doubted whether she would even have time to come to the House of Commons at all, as she had better things to do than listen to a bunch of nonentities and has-beens sucking up to Jacques Delors. In fact, when the Debate started, everything went very well. Mr Hurd gave a very interesting talk about Homer and Virgil. No one could call his brain minute, oh no! Then suddenly, oh no, there she was, in a bright pink suit which was obviously put on to show up against all the sensible grey suits that other people had chosen to wear.

But I had nothing to worry about. When she got up to speak she began: "I would just like to give my full and whole-hearted support to my honourable friend, the Prime Minister, in his splendid and inspiring opposition to Europe and all that it stands for." Everyone clapped and cheered, showing that the party is now totally united behind me.

Monday

At the Cabinet meeting this morning I was remarkably surprised by the interest shown in my Citizen's Charter. When I got out the file to brief my colleagues on the cricket scheme, I found an unsigned note on Cabinet stationery. "You asked for ideas for your Charter," it said. "Mine is drop it at once. It's a non-starter." The message was made from individual letters torn out of the newspapers, like the kidnap notes you sometimes see in *Inspector Morse*. "It could have been anyone," said Chris, when I asked for the perpetrator. "Or everyone," he added. Then they all laughed. But I will take no notice.

Clearly my Citizen's Charter is an idea ahead of its time which must be persevered with over a considerable period. "Like the Poll Tax," said Mr Waldegrave, who, I notice, had a pair of scissors in his top pocket.

Tuesday

Mrs Thatcher has given in at last and conceded that I am the Prime Minister now and that what I say goes. I rang her in America to congratulate her on this admirable and praise-worthy move.

"You will have more leisure time now", I said, "to do whatever you want."

"Yes," she agreed. "I shall be able to speak out more often on important issues like Europe, the leadership of the party and whatever else comes into my mind."

I am glad that at last she has seen sense.

Monday

I am in no small measure annoyed by the failure of my

colleagues to see the point of my Citizen's Charter. They do not seem to be able to understand that in its way the Major Charter could be as important a constitutional landmark in the history of Britain as the Magna Carta, and incidentally could win us the next election.

I seem to be the only member of the Cabinet who ever puts any suggestions into the ring-pull folder. I have thought up at least eight more in the last week alone, not counting the one about being able to get compensation from the BBC if the programmes are running late and your video fails to record the desired programme you have set it to record. I thought of this one the other night when I came back late from the House (that's what we call Parliament) to watch the Test Match highlights. But, because of the tennis overrunning due to the bad weather, all we had on the video was a repeat of *Cagney and Lacey*. My wife Norman said she enjoyed this more than she would have done watching the cricket. In this case, in my judgement, I had to admit that compensation might not have been appropriate.

Anyway, the other eight ideas I had were all of a very high standard indeed, although when I read them over the phone to my friend Chris he was not his usual enthusiastic self and said he was in a meeting. I am beginning to think that another very good suggestion for the Charter would be if someone has a really brilliant idea which none of his colleagues appreciate, then he should be entitled to compensation and a full apology from all of them, especially Mr Waldegrave.

Tuesday

I was glad to see that Chris was back on form this morning when he came in to tell me that I was going to make an important speech on the environment. I said: "Don't be silly, Chris, that's Prince Charles's job. Surely I can't have been given his job when I've only just got Mrs Thatcher's?" Chris gave me one of his looks, and passed over a folder marked "Major's Green Initiative".

When I got there I was rather surprised to be greeted by a Mr Neill, who has funny hair, who said he was very grateful to me for coming along to open his conference. As we went up onto the platform, I was rather surprised to see posters everywhere saying READ THE SUNDAY TIMES — THE PAPER THAT THINKS GREEN. "I hope this is not just a publicity stunt for your newspaper," I said to Mr Neill in the special firm voice I use for dealing with Mr Kinnock's questions about the economy. "Absolutely not, Prime Minister," he replied. "If we'd wanted publicity we would have asked Mrs Thatcher."

Wednesday

When I came down to breakfast this morning I was considerably surprised to see on my plate a small pile of dried muesli instead of my usual Shredded Wheat. When I asked Norman to pass the sugar and Gold Top, she said: "No. Mr Waldegrave doesn't allow them any more. We have to give the nation a lead in healthy eating." I said: "I'd rather starve to death than eat this." She immediately left the room, and I heard her next door ringing her friend from *Hello!* magazine to say that I had gone on hunger strike and was talking about death.

I was particularly peeved at this breakfast incident, because I knew I had another long day ahead of me, watching the Test Match. Mr O'Donnell is convinced that the more time I devote to watching cricket, the higher my rating seems to get in the polls for doing a good job as Prime Minister.

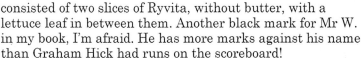

It was a very enjoyable day's work, with just one proviso — namely the packed lunch that Norman had put in my briefcase. This consisted of two slices of Ryvita, without butter, with a lettuce leaf in between them. Another black mark for Mr W. in my book, I'm afraid. He has more marks against his name than Graham Hick had runs on the scoreboard!

Thursday

This morning Mr Hurd told me that he had arranged for me to make a very important visit to China. Apparently no major foreign statesman has visited China for two years, so it will be quite a coup if I can be shown on television talking to their leaders. That is what Mr Hurd said, and moreover it would be a very good opportunity to thank them for allowing us to build an airport in Hong Kong.

Mr Hurd explained that the Chinese have their own

ancient codes of eti-
quette, and that there
are certain things
which it is impolite to
mention. To prepare me
for my talks with the
Chinese leaders, he
gave me a list of contro-
versial topics which one
should avoid in order

not to give offence. They are: "students";
"democracy"; "1989"; "massacre"; and "Tiananmen Square".

I cannot see that it will be much of a problem to keep off
these subjects. I can always talk to them about cricket!

Friday

We had a meeting of the Cabinet this morning, which will
be the last one before the holidays. Mr McGregor, who ar-
ranges these things, said that our business was finished. "So
is everyone else's," said Chris, looking pointedly at Norma
Lamont, who for a change did not laugh. Come to think of it,
he hasn't told any of his jokes for a long time. "Rubbish," said
Norma, looking very considerably annoyed. "The up-turn is
coming next week. How many more months do I have to go on
saying this before you'll all believe me?"

Monday

This is the biggest week I have had since I became Prime
Minister. First of all I have been chosen to be the host of
something called the G-7 meeting and I will finally unveil my
Citizen's Charter which everyone has been looking forward to
for many months.

I must admit that I had never heard of the "G-7" until Mr
Hurd told me that it was happening in London this year, and
that it was my big chance to shine on the world stage in time
for the next election. I had to ask him why it was called G-7.
It sounds a bit like the M6 or those garages called Q8, I said
to him. Mr Hurd handed me a glossy brochure which had
my picture on the front with the words JOHN MAJOR
WILKOMMEN DU AUS GROSSE BRITANNIEN. "It's all in
here," he said. "You can have a quick look and then pass it on
to Herr Kohl when he arrives in five minutes' time."

Before I had had time to get out my *Tourist German in
Five Minutes* phrase book, Mr O'Donnell was ushering me out

into Downing Street where there were hundreds of photographers, cameramen and security guards. At that moment 26 huge black cars drew up and out stepped Mr Bush, Mr Kohl, Mr Mitterrand, a Japanese gentleman whose name I did not know, and various other important-looking people from all over the world. When I had had my photograph taken shaking hands with them all, they went off to the hotels where they were staying, which was just as well, since I still had some finishing touches to put to my Citizen's Charter.

Tuesday

This morning I was in no small measure pleased, not to mention surprised, to see that all the newspapers had headlines such as MAJOR G-7 SUMMIT TRIUMPH, with pictures of me shaking hands with Mr Bush and the others.

When my wife Norman looked over my shoulder she asked, "What does G-7 mean, John? You still haven't explained." "Well, it's rather complicated," I told her. "You know those garages called Q8? It is rather the same sort of idea." Then I gave her a copy of Mr Hurd's brochure so that she could work it out for herself.

After breakfast, I was taken in a big car to a very important-looking building called Marlborough House, near Buckingham Palace. When I got there, there was a huge table with all our names written on special plaques and the flags of all the countries so that everyone could see where we came from. Once again there were hundreds of photographers taking pictures, but after a few minutes they were all sent out of the room, the doors were closed and Mr Bush said: "OK, John boy, let's get down to business. What's on the menu for the first session?" Everyone was looking at me, rather like we used to look at Mrs Thatcher in the Cabinet in the old days, before she went off her head and gave me her job. Fortunately, when I opened my briefcase I found all the notes I had been writing on the Citizen's Charter, which gave me a brilliant idea for something to talk about. I explained to them what the Charter was all about, and suggested that perhaps we could have a charter for all the citizens of the world.

It could deal with such matters as what happens when your baggage is sent on by the airline to another country. As things stand, the citizen has no redress about this type of mistake when it occurs across international boundaries.

When I had finished, there was a long silence which went on for a considerable period of time. Obviously they were all thinking carefully about the implications of my revolutionary proposal. Eventually Mr Typhoo, who is the Prime Minister of Japan, said that because he had not got much time, perhaps we should get on to discussing the breakdown in the GATT-round talks.

Wednesday

This morning, when we were having our next meeting round the big table, the doors were suddenly flung open and in came Mr Gorbachev. "I do not come hat in hand, gentlemen," he said. "No, it is on your head as usual," quipped Mr Bush, just as if he was Bob Hope. It seemed that Mr Gorbachev had come to borrow some money, since his country had run out. But Mr Hurd whispered to me that it had all been agreed beforehand we were not going to give him any. He then gave me a piece of paper headed "Read this out to Gorby in your special firm voice", which I did. What it said was that Russia would have to put its house in order before we could give them any cash, but that if President Gorbachev was interested in a photo-opportunity, this had been arranged for after our meeting, and could he please wait outside.

Afterwards Mr Gorbachev had his picture taken with all the other world leaders, and I was allowed to sit in the middle.

Thursday

Now that all the presidents and prime ministers have gone home, I can finally get down to the really important business of the week, the launching of my Citizen's Charter.

I was amused to see a lot of articles saying that the Charter had been "watered down", no doubt inspired by the Labour Party. Oh, no. As everyone would see, it had been very considerably toughened up, and in my judgement it has more teeth than anything the Government managed to do under Mrs Thatcher. For example, there is a whole new section laying down that in future all civil servants will have to wear name-tabs saying who they are, and when they answer the telephone to members of the public they will have to say "Have a nice day."

The Charter will also ensure that in future all trains and buses will be on time, which I am sure will be particularly welcome to harassed commuters.

Also we are appealing to commercial firms to step forward to sponsor much-loved army regiments which Mr King might otherwise have to shut down. When I gave my friend Chris a "sneak preview" of this bit, he said: "Good thinking, Prime Minister. So in future it will be the NatWest Household Cavalry and the Hoffmeister Lager Light Infantry?" "Yes," I said to him in my firm voice. "What is wrong with that?"

After lunch I again had to use my firm voice in the House of Commons, when Mr Kinnock tried to catch me out about the bank that Mr Leigh-Pemberton had to close down because it had run out of money (like Mr Gorbachev). Mr Kinnock accused me of telling a lie. I was so angry that for a very considerable period of time I could not think of anything to say. Then I had an inspiration. "If you say that, it just shows that you wouldn't be any good at being Prime Minister." Everyone cheered when I said this.

Friday

The papers this morning had huge headlines saying: TORIES SET TO WIN ELECTION AS MAJOR KOs KINNOCK

August

Monday

Today my wife Norman and I went away on our holiday. Goodbye Number 10 Downing Street. Goodbye Mr Hurd. Goodbye Mr Waldegrave. "Shouldn't that be 'au revoir'?"

asked my friend Chris. "Not in Mr Waldegrave's case," I replied.

We had decided to go to Spain as Norman says the sunshine there will do me good and perhaps I won't look so pale and ill. Also Spain is in the EC, which is very important because Mrs Thatcher used to go to Switzerland, which isn't! This shows yet again how different I am to my predecessor. Often she never took a holiday at all, because she said she didn't need it. But it didn't do her much good, did it, when after only eleven years she was forced to retire because of the strain? On the plane I started to read the new novel by my friend Jeffrey Archer. It is very long and is sure to last me the full two weeks! It is called *Esau and Jacob*, and judging by the cover it is very exciting! When we arrived at Alicante airport the Sunaway tour bus was two hours late. As I said to Norman, I hope they have a "Carta Citizeños" in Spain. She said, "I think it is the third door on the right", but it was not, so I wasn't able to register my very considerable dissatisfaction with the travel arrangements.

Tuesday

At last we are in our villa, the Villa Granada. It is very nice indeed, with a swimming pool and two Spanish maids who come in every day to look after us. The only snag is that there is no hot water in the shower unit which is, in my judgement, in blatant contravention of the description given in the Sunaway brochure. As I said to one of our maids: "We really need a Carta Citizeños." "Si, si, Señor," she agreed, showing how quick she was to see the point of my Charter idea, unlike certain of my colleagues who may find themselves having rather longer holidays with their toffee-nosed friends in Tuscany than they expected!

Anyway, imagine my surprise when Maria came back half an hour later, triumphantly announcing "Una Carta Citizeños, Señor Primo Ministero," and plonking down a large plate of what I think was fried squid.

During the afternoon I sunbathed by the pool, thus demonstrating that I am more than capable of relaxing, unlike certain of my predecessors! In fact I did not think about Mrs Thatcher for at least half an hour! While I was on my sunlounger I began to read my friend Jeffrey's book. I think it may have been the heat, because I found it very hard to get into his story about these two brothers who come from humble origins and find themselves both wanting to be prime minister!

Wednesday

Today I was looking forward to sitting by the pool, sipping the local drink which is called Pinacolada, and getting into my book. But Norman said that we should go sightseeing. She had found in the guidebook a very interesting castle in the mountains. It took us eleven hours to get there by bus, and I was very glad that I had brought Mr Archer's book to read on the journey. But unfortunately the road was so bumpy that it was very hard to concentrate, and I did not get beyond the first page. It is about two brothers who both want to be prime minister, and I am sure it will, in no small measure, turn out to be "a gripping tale of power and passion by a master storyteller" as it says on the cover.

The castle was unfortunately closed when we arrived. Norman read out the entry from her *Spain on 5,000 Pesetas a Day* guidebook, about a 16th-century duke called Don Juan the Wise, who had told his people that if they had any complaints about the way the province was administered, they could come to see him in person and he would put it right. He even laid down fixed sums to be paid in compensation if, say, an innkeeper failed to provide proper accommodation for passing pilgrims. One of the English tourists who were on the bus overheard Norman reading out this very interesting passage and said: "It sounds just like that idiot we've got at home." I wonder who he was talking about? Probably someone on the television who I have not seen.

Thursday

Although it is a great relief to be away from work, there are some aspects of it that I miss, such as going to the Test Match, which begins today. Fortunately, however, there is a radio in the villa and I was therefore able to try to tune into the BBC World Service to keep up with the score. After I had turned the knob for a considerable period of time, hearing a lot of Arabian pop music, I eventually got Radio Monte Carlo where I heard a strangely familiar voice. It was saying: "But of course when I persuaded President Bush to go to war I meant that the job should be finished. Do you think if I was still in power that we would have been feeble enough to let Mr Hussein stay alive?" Norman jumped up and tactfully moved the dial to another station. An American voice was saying: "That was John Lennon's '*Imagine*'. And now Radio Tunisia's English language service presents an exclusive interview with British Premier Margaret Hilda Thatcher." And guess what she said?

"Of course it would not be right for me to comment on the way Mr Major lost the Gulf War, especially when he is out of the country on yet another of these holidays he seems to need." I was so cross that I quite forgot about the Test Match and, turning the radio off, I returned to page one of my book.

Friday

When I had been sitting with my book by the swimming pool for a considerable number of hours this morning, Norman came out with a Diet 7-Up. She looked at me and said: "Well, John, at least no one will call you grey any more."

"Why is that?" I asked.

"Because you are bright red all over."

When I thought about it I realised that I was not feeling particularly well, so I told Norman that I would lie down inside for a while. In fact I felt quite sick and had a not insignificant headache so I was very pleased to hear Norman going to the telephone and describing my symptoms to someone in great detail. "It looks like sunstroke, which I don't need to tell you can be fatal," I heard her say. When she came back, I asked her in my special weak voice how long it would be before the doctor came. "I don't know," she said. "I was talking to a lady from a Spanish magazine called *Olé!*"

Saturday

This morning I am glad to say I felt much better, although I decided that it would perhaps be more prudent not to venture out into the sun. I was just about to have another go at starting my book, when the telephone rang, and who should it be but my friend Jeffrey Archer himself. "I see from the *Telegraph* that you are reading my new novel on holiday," he said, "and I just wanted to find out how you are getting on."

"Well, Jeffrey," I told him, "it is in my judgement a

gripping tale of power and passion by a master storyteller."

"But are you enjoying it?" he asked.

"Oh yes," I said.

Monday

It has been, in my judgement, a most historic week. Certainly more historic than last week when I was on holiday in Spain! It all began when I was listening to the news this morning and I heard that Mr Gorbachev had been suddenly taken ill and could no longer carry out his duties as President of Russia. At this point my wife Norman said: "How are you feeling, John?" I ignored her, realising at once that this was no time for me to appear in *Hello!* again. History was being made, oh yes, and I was not going to be ruled out of it by any manner

of means. I acted decisively and rang Mr Bush to ask what I should do. He was rather offhand and said he had a marlin on the line, which I presumed was a reference to his well-known spokesman Mr Fitzwalter. "Have you heard the news?" I said. "Apparently Mr Gorbachev is very ill and has had to go to prison." Mr Bush said: "Don't do or say anything, John. This calls for a measured response and not from you." I was considerably pleased that he had taken me into his confidence.

Tuesday

You can imagine that I was to no small degree irritated when I turned on the radio and television this morning to hear several interviews with guess-who holding forth in her usual strident fashion about the necessity for us all to support Mr Gorbachev in his hour of need. It is clear that she is not sufficiently important for Mr Bush to brief on this very delicate issue. What a fool she is making of herself, trying to pose as a senior world statesman on all channels at once! I was just explaining all this to Mr Hurd when the special hot-line telephone on my desk rang. There was a Russian man at the other end called Mr Yeltsin saying that he wanted to speak to Mrs Thatcher urgently. "You have got the wrong number," I said and put the phone down in no uncertain manner. Mr Hurd went white and said that I should ring him back at once, since he was the President of Russia. "Oh no he isn't," I said. "The President of Russia is Mr Yanayev. He has taken over while Mr Gorbachev is unwell." For the Foreign Secretary, Douglas is really rather behind on this one! I rang Mr Yeltsin back and explained who I was. He said that he couldn't talk to me as just at that moment some tanks were coming up the street to shoot at him. I promised that I would look into it as a matter of urgency. Then Mr Hurd suggested that it was perhaps time for me to go out into Downing Street and read out the following statement in my extra firm voice: "I want to make it very clear", I read, "that it is entirely unconstitutional to overthrow an elected leader in mid-term by means of an internal party coup." For some reason there was a certain amount of giggling at this from the journalists who do not appear to be taking this crisis with an appropriate degree of seriousness.

Wednesday

My intervention seems to have done the trick! It seems that Mr Gorbachev is much better and is able to come back to being President again. Everyone in Moscow seems to be very pleased, or so I gathered from an interview I saw being given on television by Mrs Thatcher. She is totally shameless. As soon as anything happens in the world, she rushes out into the street looking for a television camera. I decided to go out into the street to say how happy I was at the news.

Fortunately I thought of a famous quotation which seemed to sum up the mood of the moment perfectly.

"Rejoice, rejoice," I told all the journalists.

Thursday

Today must be ruled as even more historic than yesterday! I was at last able to speak to Mr Gorbachev in person. He was back on his old Kremlin number. When I got through he asked me to thank Mrs Thatcher for her wonderful support, which had made all the difference. I was just about to say something to him about this, when he went on: "And another thing. That money we talked about last month, the £5,000 billion, can you hurry up with it." I began to explain to him how important it was for him to get his economy sorted out first. "Without prudent financial management," I told him, "you could end up in a very serious recession with millions of unemployed... " As I continued with this sensible advice I was most irritated to find that I had been put on "Hold" and had to listen to the theme tune from *Dr Zhivago*. These coup people, when you think about it, may well have had a point.

Friday

Another historic day. Sri Lanka batted very poorly in my judgement and Phillip de Freitas took a considerable number of wickets. Oh yes.

At our meeting today, before the cricket, I briefed the Cabinet about what I had seen on television the night before. "These are momentous events that we are passing through," I said, quoting the words of Mr Jeremy Paxman.

"All sorts of countries which did not use to be on my *Daily Telegraph* map are now declaring their full independence."

A number of my colleagues appeared to be jet-lagged from their holidays, as they said very little during the discussion. Norma Lamont, however, asked a topical question: "What's red and under the bed?"

No one seemed to know and he answered: "Cecil Parkinson's face." Everyone laughed, though I did not see what Mr Parkinson, a former Minister, had to do with the Russian crisis.

"Gentlemen," I said, returning to my point. "All this just goes to show that you cannot run lots of countries from the centre with a vast bureaucratic regime. We must recognise these new nations at once."

Mr Hurd then intervened, saying, rather sensibly in my estimation: "I think we should not take any action until we have consulted with our EEC colleagues."

Again everyone laughed. It must be relief at all the good news from the USSR.

September

Monday

Today I went to America with Mr Hurd. Mr Hurd said that we were going on holiday with Mr Bush. "I've just been on holiday in Spain," I told him quite sternly. "I thought we had come here on business." When we arrived, Mr Bush was out in his boat playing golf, while lots of photographers flew overhead in helicopters. When he got off the boat, he looked very pleased to see me. "Stand just where you are," he said, "and look relaxed as if you're on holiday." He then gave me a baseball bat and said, "Hold this." Fortunately I had been warned that he might do this, and I gave him a special cricket bat signed by Graham Gooch. Mr Bush then turned to the hundreds of pressmen standing around and said: "John and I have had long and fruitful talks." He then said: "Gotta go, John, I'm on court with Jimbo and Mac in five minutes," and as he went off with his tennis racquet, I was in no small measure sorry to see a man in sunglasses throwing my special 333 bat into a bin marked KEEP KENNEBUNKPORT TRASH-FREE. One of Mr Bush's assistants said to me: "You did well, John, to get 30 seconds with the President." Obviously Mr Bush and I have developed a considerably special relationship! Then he added: "Even your Mrs Thatcher only got three hours when she called by yesterday." I was in no small measure irritated. Why does she keep trotting around the globe having her photo taken? It's considerably pathetic, in my judgement.

Tuesday

Back to work! I had to fly back to England to go to the Test Match against Sri Lanka. Unfortunately I had to leave before close of play to go to Russia with Mr Hurd. "This is an historic opportunity," he told me on the plane, "as you will be the first world leader to visit the new Russia."

When I got there it looked much the same as last time, except that all the statues were being taken down to be cleaned. Mr Hurd told me that we were going to see the President of Russia, but as so often he was wrong, because when we got there it was another man called Yeltsin! What a good thing I am here to hold Mr Hurd's hand in these matters of top-level diplomacy!

Mr Yeltsin welcomed me by saying that it was a pity I had not been there an hour earlier, as I could have met Mrs Thatcher, the Prime Minister of Britain, with whom he had had several hours of very useful discussions. Hundreds of cameras clicked, and then Mr Yeltsin said he was very sorry, he had to go off to run the country, but he had arranged for someone to show me round Moscow. The funny thing about our guide was that he looked exactly like Mr Gorbachev, right down to that funny red mark on his head.

Wednesday

Today Mr Hurd and I have to go to China to sign a very important contract which he has arranged to build a new airport in Hong Kong. If we promise to build the airport with our own money, then in five years' time the Chinese can have it and it won't cost them a penny. In return for their agreeing to this, Mr Hurd explained, all I had to do was avoid saying the words "Tiananmen Square" to anyone. This proved considerably difficult when I had to inspect a guard of honour in the place I wasn't allowed to mention. But I certainly got my own back in the evening when I made a speech about the collapse of communism in Russia which Mr Hurd had written out for me on the back of a napkin. The message was spelt out loud and clear, oh yes. In my special firm voice I told them: "Make no mistake. Certain things have recently been going on in certain parts of the world which could happen in certain other places, oh yes." Then a very old Chinese man at the end of the table, who I had noticed having trouble eating with chopsticks, was lifted out of his chair to make a very inscrutable speech in reply.

"We Chinese have an ancient saying," he said. "It is a great mistake to replace an old and wise leader with a younger man," he continued. "Only yesterday I was able to quote this to your leader Mrs Thatcher, when she dropped in for a Set Meal for Two Persons with myself."

Thursday

Today is Thursday so it must be Hong Kong. It is quite confusing though, since most people here

are not HongKongese but Vietnamese. Anyway conditions in this country are quite unacceptable in my judgement. All the Vietnamese people are kept in wire cages, while everyone else lives in huge tower blocks across the bay. "Something must be done," I said, reading out the rather short speech Mr Hurd had given me in my most caring voice.

I then gave the Vietnamese leader a special Souvenir of the Sri Lanka Test cricket bat to mark the occasion of my historic visit. "At least Mrs Thatcher hasn't been here first," I joked to Mr Hurd. "No," he said. "You wouldn't find her in Hong Kong trying to explain to 6,000 angry businessmen why we've sold them down the river. That's your job."

He then handed me yet another speech marked "Read out in your apologetic voice." In fact the speech went quite well. The businessmen all threw spring rolls at me, which Mr Hurd explained is an old Chinese way of showing appreciation to an honoured visitor from across the sea.

Friday

Home again! While I was waiting for my luggage to come round on the carousel, a cheery voice broke in at my elbow. It was my friend Chris. "Great news, John!" he cried. "Since you went away we've gone up five points in the polls. If you stayed away for another three months, we might even win the election."

Saturday

I read in the paper there is going to be a general election. "Fever is mounting," I said to my wife Norman, who immediately slipped out to ring her aunt, or so she said. "Hello?" she said. "I've got a scoop for you." She must have been referring to her new ice-cream maker that Mrs Bush gave her in America.

Later on at my Cabinet meeting Mr Waldegrave sidled up to me and asked in a hushed voice: "Well, John, is it November?" "No," I sighed. "It is still September and will be for some considerable period of time." You do expect your Ministers (or ex-Ministers as looks increasingly probable in his case!) to know what month we are in. Oh yes.

After lunch I announced to the Cabinet that I had made a firm decision about the election. "I have decided that I have not made up my mind." They all shook their heads in agreement, which was very gratifying. No wonder I am ahead in the polls.

Monday

I am considerably delighted that my tour of the world, meeting famous world leaders, has been a great success. I am now 4 per cent ahead in the polls and apparently when the voters are asked "Which party leader is the most convincing world statesman?" only 2 per cent named Mr Kinnock, whereas my rating of 28 per cent was within striking distance of Mr Ashdown on 74 per cent. He, of course, has the advantage of having been in the SAS, which the pollsters do not take into account when they ask their questions. Besides which, I have been away and people may have forgotten who I am. When I came into the office this morning, my friend Chris said: "John, I hope it's spring?" Obviously Chris has been working too hard on winning the election, and I had to point out to him quite firmly that it was, if he cared to look out of the window, still autumn.

Tuesday

At the Cabinet meeting today Mr Baker said: "Well, Prime Minister, I think it's time to go."

"Kenneth," I said, "we shall certainly miss you, but I think you have made the right decision."

For the first time in my memory, the considerably annoying smile vanished instantly from his by no means unsmug face. "No Prime Minister," he said, "I am talking about the election." At this everyone started to talk at once, and eventually I had to shut them up. I promised that I would make up my mind about an autumn election by March at the latest.

Wednesday

Today I took the decision. I would definitely stay in tonight so that Norman and I could have a romantic candlelit Sainsbury's Chicken Tikka dinner in front of the TV play about how we got rid of Mrs Thatcher. I have to say that I was very considerably disappointed. For a start the actor who was meant to be playing me was very wooden and uninspiring. He totally lacked charisma. Also they got everything completely wrong. When they had a whole scene showing me in bed reading a novel by Jeffrey Archer, I did not

have the top button of my pyjamas undone, as they showed. I always do up all my buttons, as a simple phone call to Mr O'Donnell could easily have found out. Honestly! What's the use of having buttons if you do not use them!

Thursday

Mr O'Donnell is certainly, in my judgement, an extraordinary man. Last night he predicted, tapping his nose with his finger, that there would be good news for me in tomorrow's papers and, when I looked at them this morning, he was absolutely right! He must be psychic because of his Irish blood! All the papers had the same headline — "Kinnock Can't Win — But Refuses To Quit, Thank Goodness." This is very good news, and at the Cabinet meeting everyone congratulated me. "Everything points to autumn, Prime Minister," said Mr Hurd. "Oh yes," I said. "There is quite a chill in the air and the leaves are quite distinctly turning to gold."

"The election, for heaven's sake," said Mr Hurd. "We are all waiting for you to make up your mind." "I shall make up my mind when I have decided to do so," I said, in my special stern voice, which so terrified Mr Deng in China that he dropped the noodles off his chopsticks. That showed them who is the boss around here!

Friday

My friend Chris came in first thing this morning to say that he had got a brilliant new angle for our campaign against Mr Kinnock. We should all make speeches saying that Mr Kinnock is just a dim political lightweight with no real principles who has abandoned the politics of conviction in an attempt to move his party into the bland middle ground of opportunistic compromise. "Well done, Chris," I said. "That should certainly make it obvious what the difference is between our party and theirs."

Saturday

This morning there was a knock on the door and a man gave me £2 million in an old suitcase. What a kind thought! I had never met Mr Latsis before but he told me he is a Greek philanthropist rather like our Jeffrey Archer. This is quite a recommendation, in my judgement.

Minutes later there was another knock at the door and another kind man whom I had never met gave me a postal order for £1 million. He said his name was Mr Lik-ah-Sing, I think, though he had a strong Chinese accent and it was difficult to tell.

Anyway, this is one in the eye for Mr Kinnock. How can he claim that there is no investment in this country when so many foreign businessmen are willing to invest in the Conservative Party?

Let him answer that if he can.

Sunday

My friend Chris tells me that today we are four points down in the polls — back to where we were when Mrs Thatcher was in charge.

"That shows I am just as popular as she was," I told him and he gave me one of his funny looks.

Monday

As I was puzzling over a memo from Mr Hurd explaining the difference between Slovenia, Slavonia and Slovakia, there was a knock at my door and a tall grey-haired man in a mackintosh came in, saying that his name was Ian McKeller and that he had an appointment with me. "We want our rights," he said. "We want to be treated just like everyone else. Don't you realise that one in six members of your Cabinet are gay?"

"Oh, no," I said, "we are all gay in my Cabinet — we laugh a good deal, particularly when Norma Lamont is telling one of his jokes." I proceeded to illustrate this point by telling my visitor the one about the three Guardsmen, the camel and the cucumber.

My visitor did not laugh but told me that I was in his judgement a "homophobe, just like Mrs Thatcher". "Oh, no," I said, "I am not like her in any respect. By the way, what is a homophobe?" When he told me that it was someone who hated homosexuals because he was secretly afraid he was one himself, I sent him packing in no uncertain terms — although before he went I assured him that, as a minority, the homosexual community would have my very sympathetic support in the run-up to the election.

No sooner had he kissed me warmly than an excitable French lady pushed her way into the room, crying: "C'est vrai! When I said zat one in four of ze English was un pouffe, I was wrong. You are all as bent as ze spoons of Uri Geller."

I was quite frankly amazed when Mr O'Donnell told me later that this lady was the Prime Minister of France. It all goes to show, in my judgement, that women are quite unsuited to be prime minister.

Tuesday

All the papers are saying that I should make up my mind about when the next election should be. They say I am dithering. I wonder if they are right? I spent a considerable period of time wondering about this, and eventually I decided to ask someone's advice. The question was, who? After another considerable period of time, I decided to ask my wife Norman who would be the best person to ask. She said: "Why don't you ask your friend Norma Lamont. He is the one who is so good at predicting the future." "Oh yes," I said, "that is a brilliant idea. Why are you laughing?"

I went next door to ask Norma Lamont when would be the best time to hold an election. "When the economy comes right, Prime Minister," he replied. "And when will that be?" I asked him, pinning him down with my inquisitorial voice that so frightens Mr Kinnock at Question Time. "Whenever you call an election," he said. Running a country is much easier than people think.

Wednesday

My friend Chris came round to see me with an idea he had thought up in the bath. "Tomorrow is Mr Kinnock's big speech at the Labour conference," he said. "Let's mess it up for him by announcing that there isn't going to be an election. Then we will get all the headlines and Kinnock will look silly. I'll tell Mr Wakeham to arrange it."

Thursday

Chris was right! We have certainly got the headlines this

morning: WAKEHAM RINGS UP TORY HACKS IN PATHETIC ATTEMPT TO SPOIL KINNOCK'S BIG SPEECH. And that was just the *Telegraph*. All the other papers had the same story, with lots of pictures of Mr Kinnock looking really unhappy and embracing Mrs Kinnock for comfort.

At the Cabinet meeting later, my friend Chris congratulated me on my very wise decision not to have an election. "Labour is eight points ahead in the polls," he said. "Thank goodness we made our announcement when we did."

Everyone laughed, especially Mr Wakeham, whose face went considerably red with pleasure.

Friday

Today I had to go to Holland for a very important meeting about Europe. The Dutch prime minister, who Mr Lamont tells me is called Mr Lewd Rubbers, has come up with a new plan for a totally united Europe immediately. When Mr Rubbers announced this, he added that he knew one country would be against it, giving me a pointed look. But when the time came to vote, he looked not inconsiderably surprised when everyone in the room raised their hands against him.

"Well," I said. "We are all united. We don't want to be united."

This is a terrific breakthrough. Mrs Thatcher would never have been able to achieve this sort of consensus.

October

Monday

This is the week of our big conference and I am very considerably worried about it. The Labour Party has reached new depths today, telling everyone that I intend to privatise the Health Service. This is a complete lie. That is Mr

Mr Waldegrave's job (one which, incidentally, he may not be in for too much longer).

Tuesday

Labour are still calling me a ditherer but there is one thing I have always been firm about. I will not bring in "image-makers" to tell me what to wear and how to speak, oh no! I rely on trusted party colleagues who advise me on such things. According to Mr Reece, who came to our Cabinet meeting and who is an expert in these areas, I should lower my voice and wear a suit.

"How about a blue twin set and a new handbag?" said my friend Chris, who was at the meeting.

How silly can you get? If I did this I would look just like Mrs Thatcher, who is coming to the conference on Wednesday.

Not that that worries me at all. I told Chris: "What ex-Prime Ministers do is of no interest to me."

"It should be," said Mr Baker, giving me his considerably annoying smile. "Labour are now seven points ahead."

Monday

I am beginning to think that all the papers are very considerably biased against the Conservative Party. This morning Mr O'Donnell came to our by no means unluxurious suite at the Imperial Hotel to show us both (me and my friend Jeffrey Archer) the headlines. They all said MAGGIE'S TRIUMPH HIGHLIGHT OF CONFERENCE. What rubbish! When she got the 25-minute standing ovation, who do they think was on the platform next to her? So by my calculation, at least 12.5 minutes of the ovation were directly attributable to myself. But do they point this out? Oh no. Wait till I make my big speech tomorrow. Then they will see what a highlight really means!

Tuesday

It was a very long night for me. It must have been at least 11.15 before I got to bed, after we had been writing my big speech. Jeffrey has come up with the most brilliant jokes. For instance, he suggests that I should say: "Kinnock, Kinnock, who's there?" And then, when I've paused, I reply: "It'll be me, after the next election!" Another really good one was about the way I sometimes say "Oh yes." Jeffrey suggested that I should refer to my education and say: "Well at least I've got six O-Yes levels." He really is a genius! At last it was ready for me to read out to my wife Norman, who is my severest critic. She said it was as good as anything I had ever done, which I think is the highest praise she has ever given me.

Tuesday night — very late (10.15)

What a successful day. My speech was acclaimed on all sides as a triumph because it was such a complete contrast to Mrs Thatcher. Whereas she was dominating, forceful and in complete command of the conference, I represented a very welcome change. The delegates showed their appreciation of the new style by avoiding the embarrassing and unnecessary scenes of wild applause and enthusiasm that had so marred previous conferences.

Wednesday

Oh dear. It is a bit of a come-down after my "Quiet Conference Triumph" as the *Daily Telegraph* called it, to have to get back to talking about the Health Service. Today I nailed the Labour lie once and for all, and I expect I will have to go on doing so right up until the election. As I told the Cabinet: "So long as I am prime minister, the Health Service is safe." My friend Chris made one of his funny faces and everyone laughed. I expect they were amused by Mr Waldegrave's new haircut. I told him to get it cut on the advice of Mr Reece. "A man with a woolly hairstyle", said Mr Reece, "looks like a man with woolly ideas." Now Mr Waldegrave is much more convincing.

Norma Lamont announced that he was going off to Bangkok for a very important economic summit. "Another chance for you to massage the figures," said Mr Mellor, who is something of a wag. We all laughed again, though I've no idea why.

Thursday

Today I really surprised everyone by showing that my Citizen's Charter is no mere election-winning gimmick, as everyone seems to think. When British Rail announced that they were going to put up all the fares, I said: "Oh no, you're not." They said: "Oh yes, we are," just like they do in the pantomimes at the Huntingdon Hippodrome, with Gareth Hunt from the coffee commercial and Miss Jan Leeming as Dick Whittington. Anyway, after we'd had a bit of an argument, they caved in and offered a compromise. All the fares would go up except the ones in my constituency. This is the kind of thing which would never have happened under Mrs Thatcher, because she went everywhere by car.

Friday

Today I went with Mr Hurd to the beautiful country of Harare for the Commonwealth Conference. This is the one where Mrs Thatcher used to get into such trouble by arguing with everybody about South Africa. But this time it is completely different. We are all agreed that South Africa should be allowed to play test match cricket as soon as possible. Mr Hurd said: "They may not have as many blacks in their team as we do, but they will have about the same number of South Africans." My first important meeting was with the South African leader Mr Mandela, with whom I had breakfast. We found we had a lot in common, especially on the subject of Mrs Thatcher, whom neither of us considered a particularly impressive world leader. We agreed to have lunch sometime, which we did a few hours later. Over lunch we found that we shared a mutual disregard for Mrs Thatcher, and we agreed to continue our conversation over dinner. That evening I was delighted to see my new friend Mr Mandela sitting next to me once again. We agreed that one thing had united the Commonwealth — the demise of Mrs Thatcher. "At least that's one dictator gone," I said, by way of a joke. "Now for the rest." Mr Hurd kicked me very hard under the table, and whispered that I should keep to the subject of cricket on which I was a not inconsiderable authority.

Saturday

The sun is shining and it is a glorious day. I never thought I would live to see Mrs Thatcher admit she has made a mistake. But now it has happened over the Television Franchise auction which a friend of hers at TV-am has lost. We were all watching in the hotel TV lounge and it was the first item on *Hello Harare*, their popular six o'clock news programme. The newsreader announced that Mrs Thatcher, the British Prime Minister, had acknowledged that she had made a terrible error of judgement. They all looked at me and one of them said: "It's a bit late to do anything about it now."

Sunday

I am becoming increasingly sick of the BBC, which continues to suggest that, like Mrs Thatcher, I want to privatise the NHS. I am entirely unlike Mrs Thatcher in this regard, which is why I have decided to send off a strongly worded letter of complaint to the BBC. "That's what Mrs Thatcher used to do," said Norman, to my even more considerable annoyance.

Sunday

I have been in no small measure impressed by Mr Heseltine of late. His speech to the Conference got a terrific round of applause and he is obviously very popular with the ordinary party members, nearly as popular in fact as my friend Jeffrey. I said as much to my friend Chris and suggested that Mr Heseltine should be given a more important job. "Like leader?" he said. I explained to Chris that such rivalries were all in the past and Mr Heseltine was now a loyal member of my team, just as I was a loyal member of Mrs Thatcher's. Chris gave me one of his funny looks.

Monday

My wife Norman clearly got out of bed the wrong side this morning. Nothing I did seemed to be right for her. "Why are you still wearing that old grey suit?" she said. "There are plenty of other grey suits upstairs for you to choose from. You men are all the same. Unless a woman tells you what to do you cannot make up your mind."

"That is not true," I replied as I went upstairs to change my suit, but she insisted on continuing the argument, which in my judgement was getting us nowhere. "Why don't you have a charter for women? You have one for everyone else. And besides," she said, handing me my CBI tie and matching handkerchief, "we women have been pushed around for long enough."

Tuesday

This morning I told the Cabinet of my new idea, i.e. that there should be more opportunities for women. My friend Chris asked: "Does this mean women in the very top jobs, John?" "Oh yes," I replied, at which point they all started laughing. I

said it was time to put an end to old-fashioned chauvinist attitudes. Norma Lamont agreed and said we should have some women in the Cabinet. There were many outstanding women he said who needed a leg-up. Mr Mellor sniggered. Norma went on to name Virginia Bottomley as someone who he had always admired for her political skills. When I suggested that Mrs Angela Rumbold was another good candidate he seemed less enthusiastic. Still it is a start. Someone called Pamella Bordes was also mentioned though I stated that I was unaware of her current position. They all began sniggering again, which made me not inconsiderably annoyed. Sometimes my colleagues do not seem to realise how important these Charters are.

Wednesday

Norman was in a better mood today and gave me an extra helping of Coco Pops which are in my judgement the best breakfast currently available. "Well," she said, "what charter have you got for us all today?" It was good to see her taking an interest in my work and I was glad to give her the details of my Health Charter which Mr Waldegrave thought up last week in an attempt to get into my good books after his haircut.

If I was due to have an operation, I explained, I would not want to be kept waiting indefinitely without knowing how long the wait would be. Under the provisions of the new Charter, I would be entitled to ring up the hospital and demand to be told the exact duration of the wait, e.g. ten years. This would be a great comfort to any NHS patient.

"Don't be silly," said Norman, "we're on BUPA. We

have been ever since the Chartered Bank started up the payments."

Undoubtedly there is much to be said for women going out to work.

Thursday

It is an exciting day for me as it is the opening of Parliament by Her Majesty the Queen. She is walking proof, I said to Norman, that women *can* get to the top of their chosen fields. The Queen is a remarkable woman. In her speech, she came up with all the same ideas as me, including a lot of new Charters.

I also made a speech at some considerable length to whomsoever was present in the Chamber. I noticed at one point that one of our Members had fallen asleep, presumably through exhaustion. It is all very well for Junior Doctors to complain about long hours, but what about Senior Backbenchers? Perhaps we should have a Charter for them too.

Friday

Some people are trying to claim that we are divided on the question of Europe. This is quite untrue. For example when Mr Tebbit said that we were trying to sell Britain down the river, the whole Cabinet agreed that he might have a point but it would be wrong to say so publicly.

Mr Hurd tells me that we have to go to a place called Maastricht quite soon and sign a new European agreement. When I asked him what the agreement was he said it was a promise by Britain that, unlike everyone else, we would move slowly forward, very slowly indeed and that in the end it was a matter for our children.

"Why should they be involved?" I queried. "They are not even old enough to vote." Mr Hurd looked considerably irritated. These Oxford people do not like to be contradicted, especially when they have made an obviously silly point.

November

Saturday

Even though it is Saturday, Mr O'Donnell says I have to work today. I have to go to Twickenham and watch the Rugby Cup Final. It is a far cry from cricket, with many more men and a much larger ball, which in my judgement is squashed. The rules are very complicated, unnecessarily so, I feel, and they will come under consideration in a future Sporting Charter.

During the match Mr O'Donnell explained that the England team had been criticised as being boring. I told him that this was no bad thing in public life and that they would probably win, by a small margin. Oh yes.

By the way, another thing struck me at the game, namely that there were no women in the England team at all.

Tuesday

Today is Guy Fawkes Night and Mr Lamont invited us all to the next door garden for a bonfire party and what he calls "A Big Bang". As we gathered round the fire to see the guy being burned, my friend Chris said that it was very unfair on Guy Fawkes, who had been quite a decent chap. Wasn't it time, he suggested, that we had someone else to burn every year? I agreed and said that, in this age of Equal Opportunities, it should be a woman. Furthermore, I could think of a very suitable candidate, oh yes!

Thursday

No one takes any serious notice of poor Mr Tebbit any more. He cuts a sad figure appearing on the television every night telling me not to go into Europe. No one listens to him and everyone knows that he is just a mouthpiece for Mrs Thatcher, who is afraid to speak out on her own.

This was quite obvious when she made a speech in America saying that I should not accept the F-word in Europe.

Norma Lamont in our Cabinet meeting today disagreed. He said that it was high time that we told Mrs Thatcher to F-off. They all laughed, but I could not see myself how anyone could Federal off. It is entirely ungrammatical and just shows how overrated all this university education really is.

Friday

Chris woke me up this morning to say that he had great news about the by-elections. Apparently we lost all three, but not by nearly as much as we could have done. "In many ways," he said, "it was a victory" — which, coincidentally, was a view shared by all the newspapers. Mr Kinnock was clearly

rattled by these results and I later saw him on the television drinking champagne and dancing around saying "No. 10, here we go" in an attempt to put a brave face on his defeat. I was particularly interested to see that the Labour Party had won in Kincardineshire. I looked this place up on my *Daily Telegraph* wall map and after a very considerable period of time I discovered it was in a place called Scotland. I decided to call in the Secretary of State for Scotland for a full explanation, but then I realised that I could not remember his name.

Sunday

Today I knew there was something very important I had to remember, but I forgot what it was. Then my wife reminded me by saying: "It's Remembrance Sunday, John. I've laid out your grey poppy to go with your suit." I have always enjoyed watching this very special ceremony on television, and particularly the moment when Mrs Thatcher steps up to place her wreath on the war memorial. But this year it will be me! Mrs Thatcher will have to stand in the background and remain completely silent for two minutes. It will be quite a strain for her, I imagine! She always used to say that Remembrance Sunday was particularly important for her, as she was the only prime minister who had led the country to victory in war. But now it is no longer true. Oh no! I refer of course to my defeat of Saddam Hussein. The thought of this should certainly make her very cross!

Monday

This morning in the Cabinet Mr Mellor said: "Well, Prime Minister, today is a very special day when we remember the fallen." "Don't be silly," I told him. "That was yesterday." "No," he said. "It is exactly a year since

we got rid of Mrs Thatcher." Everyone laughed, except Mr Heseltine who for some reason looked rather glum. Undoubtedly David is a funny man and I am proud to have him in my team. He is just the sort of man we could do with to present our case on the Health Service, since everyone is saying it is a joke.

Tuesday

Mr O'Donnell came in this afternoon to say that a very important newspaper proprietor called Robert Maxwell had died, and that it would be a good idea if I paid a tribute to him to get on The World At One.

Oh yes, I said, I remember him well. He was very helpful to me when I went to Russia. He gave me the name of a key contact of his who I should be sure to look up when I got to Moscow. It turned out to be Mr Gorbachev. When I told Mr Gorbachev that I knew Mr Maxwell, he gave me a large suitcase full of money and asked me to take it to him. I was happy to oblige. Mr O'Donnell said he liked the Gorbachev angle, but said that perhaps I should not go into too much detail as it would make the tribute too long.

Wednesday

Britain has always been a proud and independent nation. We will not be told what to do by any foreign power whomsoever, like the Germans. In my judgement, we must make our own decisions. I said this to Mr Bush when he rang me this morning to tell me that the Libyans were guilty over this plane crash and we were going to introduce sanctions at once. Would I implement the necessary procedures forthwith, or, as he put it in his colourful language, "Shift butt, John, and pronto." I immediately decided, with *no* consultation of my European partners *note*, that sanctions should be applied on Libya at once.

Monday

A very delightful surprise greeted me when I arrived home this evening from the House (of Parliament — not my house obviously or I could not have returned from there!). Anyway, there was no sign of Norman and all the lights were off. Luckily I had my pencil torch-and-screwdriver set in my top pocket, so I immediately went to the fuse-box which is in the cupboard under the stairs where I keep such useful items as my old cricket pads.

When I opened the door, however, who should I find but Norma Lamont with his new research assistant. "Oh, hullo Prime Minister," he said, "we were hoping to surprise you rather than the other way about." At that moment there was a lot of giggling and the whole Cabinet came out of hiding, all wearing paper hats except for Mr Hurd. My friend David Mellor explained that he and Chris had planned a special party to celebrate my first year as Prime Minister. They had even laid on a big cake with one candle on it, to commemorate all my, by no means inconsiderable, achievements. There was a rather clever message on top of the cake — A YEAR WITH-OUT THE OLD BAT — a reference no doubt to my well-known love of cricket. The party went on till all hours and it must have been at least half-past nine before I got to bed.

Tuesday

Today is my big day, when I have to tell the House of Commons exactly where I stand on the famous Maastricht negotiations. Mr Hurd was very kind and gave me a 15-page outline of what I should say. He had guessed my thoughts so accurately that I didn't have to change a single word. The best bit (what Mr O'Donnell called "a great sound-bite") was where I said: "We

have built the station. The train has left. It is high time we got on board, unless we decide to get off." When I said this in the House of Commons they all cheered except you-know-who, who spoilt the effect by getting up and making a very long speech which nobody listened to. I feel quite sorry for her, really.

Wednesday

It was in no small measure irritating when I read in the papers a whole lot of headlines such as MAGGIE KOs FEEBLE MAJOR and THATCHER'S REFERENDUM CALL — LET MY PEOPLE CHOOSE. I cannot think why the newspapers pay so much attention to what Mrs Thatcher says, when she's not even Prime Minister any longer. I certainly don't, which is why I immediately proved it by asking Mr O'Donnell to tell all the newspapers that there is definitely not going to be a referendum. This should leave no one in any doubt as to whom is in charge, and should shut her up once and for all.

Thursday

Imagine my surprise when I turned on the television at lunchtime to see Mrs Thatcher once again holding forth, and actually having the cheek to say that I was "arrogant" not to go along with her referendum idea. Quite clearly she is, as usual, totally out of touch with what ordinary people think. And as for her calling people "arrogant" , well all I can say is that I am speechless. "I feel quite sick," I told Norman, who immediately went off to ring up her friend at *Hello!* magazine.

Friday

The newspapers have once again got it all wrong. They have brought out an opinion poll which says that 87 per cent of the public are in favour of Mrs Thatcher's referendum scheme. How can ordinary people be expected to understand something as complicated as the Common Currency and European Monetary Union? Even I don't understand it, and I am Prime Minister (unlike some people I can think of !)

Saturday

Today it has been decided that as part of my schedule I should be seen relaxing at a football match with my friend David Mellor. The game was in Chelsea and David and I were lucky enough to get very good seats, right next to where all the photographers were sitting. While I was enjoying the game, I couldn't help thinking how bad Mrs Thatcher was at relaxing, and how much better I am at doing it. Watching sport, in my judgement, is a good way to take your mind off

politics. When I made this point to David, he said: "Shut up, John, the Blues have just scored." It is interesting, I thought, that Chelsea have exactly the same colours, i.e. blue, as the Conservative Party. Perhaps, I said to David, this is a good omen for the next election. Unfortunately he was distracted as the other side had scored twice and won the game.

December

Monday

A very successful dinner party was held last night in my honour. A number of Asian businessmen had very kindly organised a grand celebration at Number Ten to commemorate my first year in office. I said to my friend Chris that this would show once and for all that the Conservatives were in no way racialist and that we have the full support of the ethnic minorities. "Quite right," said Chris. "We will take money from anyone."

I did not understand this but assumed he meant that these businessmen and their shops provide a valuable late-night service with groceries etcetera.

This was perhaps why Mr Patten made a number of references in his speech to credit cards being accepted or cheques being taken provided there was a number written on the back.

Some of the businessmen clearly misunderstood him and took out huge wads of money and asked questions about the honours list.

In my judgement, these people still have much to learn.

Tuesday

Mr Lamont brings good news about our negotiations with the EEC. Apparently we don't have to opt out of the common currency after all! We have also secured another important concession. The Queen's head will continue to be on our coins and bank notes. For example, the 5-ecu piece will have the EEC symbol on one side and the head of Jacques Delors on the other. This is what happens when there are tough negotiations!

And there will be more. As I said to the Cabinet: "It is hard pounding." Mr Waldegrave added: "But not hard ecuing then?" All the others laughed, which was very considerably annoying given the gravity of the situation.

Talking of troublemakers, I have told Mrs Thatcher on the phone that she has to keep out of the limelight during the run-up to the General Election. "You can rely on me," she said with a slight laugh, which was clearly a nervous reaction to my admonishment.

I am sure this has done the trick.

Sunday

Today is the big day I have been waiting for for six months. Mr Hurd is going to tell me what my plan is for the conference at Maastricht. To celebrate I have bought a special new retractable biro to sign the agreement with — if I sign, that is! On the plane to Holland, which I gather is famous for its tulips (though not obviously at this time of year!) they gave us a very nice lunch, even though it was tea-time. While I was trying to undo all the bits of plastic to get at my pastry, Mr Hurd came to sit next to me. "Prime Minister," he said, "it is time to talk Turkey." "Oh," I said. "I was not aware that they are members of the European Community." Mr Hurd looked considerably cross at being caught out again by a non-Oxford man! But he quickly went on to say: "Our aim, John, must be to achieve unity at all costs." "Oh," I replied, "I did not think that you were so much of a Europhile?" "No, you idiot, I mean Prime Minister!" he snapped. "Forget Europe. I was thinking about the Party." I did not realise that they had been planning a party to celebrate the signing (if I sign!). But I kept quiet since Mr Hurd looked rather ill at this point, no doubt due to what they call jet lag!

When we had been to our hotel, which was a very attractive modern building made of concrete in the shape of two tulips on each side of a windmill, we went out to a dinner party with my friend Herr Kohl. I was sitting next to Mrs Kohl, whose first name is Frau (like a lot of German ladies, I have noticed). She was a very interesting person to talk to, as she asked me to explain the rules of "your English game cricket". We got along famously. I was able to use the salt and pepper to

represent the stumps, and I was just getting to the new front-foot rule when I couldn't help overhearing what Mr Hurd was saying to President Kohl. "So unless you give us a couple of opt-outs there'll be such an uproar that you'll find Maggie back at Number Ten with Ridley as Foreign Secretary." "Achtung, Schweinhund!" he cried, just like Richard Burton does in *Where Eagles Dare* (which is, incidentally, one of my favourite films, though not Norman's). "What's all this?" I said in my special firm voice, which woke Mrs Kohl up. "What are you two talking about?" "Oh nothing," said Herr Kohl. "Let us drink to your triumph tomorrow!" Whereupon he stood up, clicked his heels and shouted: "Deutschland Uber Alles!", which is apparently the German for "Cheers".

Monday

This morning we went to the place where the famous conference is taking place. It is in a very attractive modern building made of bricks, in the shape of two windmills on each side of a tulip. To get there we had to go in a boat, because the conference centre is on an island. We immediately got down to some very hard negotiating, with Mr Hurd and Mr Lamont explaining to all the foreign people why they had got it all wrong. For a start, they have spelt the Social Charter with a P! In my judgement, this kind of silly mistake is all too typical of the slapdash approach of these Europeans. I handled the toughest part of all, which was the "single currency" issue. My job was to read out a speech which Mr

Hurd had written for me in twelve languages. As I said to them, "No, Non, Nein, Ochi, Nyet, Etc," which I suspect is the Portuguese for "no". My courageous stand had the desired effect. After twelve hours of this, the foreigners all looked at their watches, laughed and said "OK — that's enough time to make it look good, let's sign." Mr Kohl then handed round a leather-bound book with, printed on the front, THE GRAND TREATY OF MAASTRICHT 1991. Inside were all the agreements with the words "except for Great Britain" printed under each of them. I was considerably impressed at the speed with which our Dutch friend Herr Lewd Rubbers (as Mr Lamont calls him) had managed to do the printing so quickly. Herr Kohl winked at Mr Hurd and pointed to me, obviously impressed by the great triumph I had just pulled off. The new biro performed as well as I had hoped, and I decided there and then that I would have it put in a special glass case at Chequers next to the one that Mr Chamberlain used at Munich.

Afterwards the journalists were allowed to come over to the island to be told what had happened, although most of them, for some reason, seemed to know already. Indeed several of them had already managed to have their articles printed, under the headline OH YES — IT'S A TRIUMPH FOR MAJOR.

Wednesday

When I told the House of Commons about my great triumph, all our side rose to their feet and waved their papers in the air. Mr Kinnock tried to ruin it by saying that I had totally failed and that Britain was now completely left out of Europe. I soon put him down with a devastating riposte which left him speechless. "Oh no we haven't," I told him (been left out, that is) and everyone cheered again. It all goes to show, as I said to Norma later over a celebratory glass of a special Dutch drink which I had bought in the Duty Free called Avocado: "This only goes to show once again how totally different I am from Mrs Thatcher. She would never have dared to go to a European summit and come away empty-handed, having disagreed with all the other eleven countries. Oh no."

Monday

This week I am facing a not inconsiderable dilemma. It is very hard to know what day it is when there are so many holidays. It feels like Sunday today, but my diary says it is Monday. This is my new Chelsea FC Supporters Club Diary which my friend David Mellor gave me for Christmas. It is very useful indeed, as it has a complete list of all the fixtures for the New Year. "Except the election," said David, with his usual brilliant wit.

My other Christmas presents were a set of my favourite biros from Rymans from my wife Norman and another copy of his new book from Jeffrey Archer. He had signed it "To Roger. Happy Birthday. June '91". His jokes are almost as good as David's.

Tuesday

We set the alarm very early today so as not to miss an important radio programme. But it was wrongly tuned and Norman and I both had a nasty shock when we heard the voice of Brian Redhead on the Today programme, who in our judgement we are not in the smallest degree in favour of. He was asking Norma Lamont in his usual rude way *when* the recession was going to end. As if anyone knew that!

Anyway, we soon found the programme we wanted: Norman's Radio 2 selection of her favourite tunes. As we listened in bed, we drank a cup of the finest Typhoo tea from our new Teasmade, a present from a Mr Ranjit Patel who sent it round in a Rolls Royce with a charming card saying "Don't forget the New Year's Honours." As if I would! Norman and I make a special point of turning to the list first when they print it in the *Daily Mail*.

Norman's selection of music was, to an unbiased observer, extremely interesting and original. I recognised a great many of the classical works. There was the theme from the World

Cup, the Lloyds Bank tune, the Hamlet Cigar music and the British Airways duet. Altogether it was a most agreeable pot-pourri, as the announcer said at the end. No one can accuse us of being Philistines, a charge which was levelled with no small measure of appropriateness at my predecessor and her husband.

(New Year Resolution: I am not going to mention Mrs Thatcher ever again.)

Wednesday

Mrs Thatcher is on television talking about Mr Gorbachev who has resigned on the grounds that he no longer has any useful role whatsoever. I have to admit that this is the one subject on which she is well qualified to talk!

It is also appropriate, I remarked to Jeffrey Archer at our drinks party at Chequers, that Mr Gorbachev should be going out with the old year and Mr Yeltsin should be coming in. "A change of leadership is absolutely essential," I said. Everyone agreed with me and Chris Patten raised his glass and gave me one of his funny looks.

Thursday

I hate to say this but Mr O'Donnell is failing in his job. There have been more stories in the papers this week suggesting that Norma Lamont and I have differences of opinion over the economy. What nonsense this is! We are both in total agreement. We have no idea what to do.

Norma has come up with the brilliant plan of abolishing stamp duty. I suppose this is because more and more people are using fax machines. Still, I cannot see how this will help home owners pay their mortgages.

Friday

I am very excited, as our Christmas holiday treat consists of an outing to Wembley. I put on my blue scarf and my rosette and go to a quick Cabinet meeting to discuss the economy before I set off.

"Oh," said Mr Hurd, wearing his most snooty expression and noting my rosette, "have we started the election campaign already?"

Sometimes he is very stupid, as is often the way with people who have had too much education.

"No," I told him, "I am off to see Chelsea play Turandot, who are, I believe, an Italian team."

"Most amusing, Prime Minister," said Mr Hurd. "I hope the *score* is satisfactory." They all laughed, especially Mr Waldegrave who nearly choked. This just goes to show how well we all get on in the Cabinet, unlike the days of my predecessor whom I never mention any more (see above!).

January 1992

Monday

The election campaign has started. I read it in the *Daily Telegraph* this morning, so it's official! After breakfast, my friend Chris came round to show me the new poster he has been working on for the past year. "This should knock Kinnock for six," he said. His poster showed a large bomb, ready to explode, with the caption VOTE CONSERVATIVE. He explained that the bomb was meant to represent Labour's secret plan to win the election by putting up taxes. He said: "Do you realise, John, that anyone earning over £30,000 will be clobbered?" "That means you and me," I replied, rather shocked. After a moment's thought, Chris said: "But then we'll both be out of a job, so it won't affect us." I felt greatly relieved.

Tuesday

In the Cabinet meeting, Norma Lamont was far from being his usual irrepressible self. Indeed he looked very considerably out of sorts. "Gentlemen," he said, "I have a confession to make to you all." For some reason everyone sniggered, except me. "What is it, Norma?" I asked him in the sort of caring voice that some prime ministers never had. "I'm afraid I have miscalculated about the economy. You know I told you all that the recovery had started? Well" — and here he burst into tears — "I'm afraid there isn't going to be one. I just made it up so that you would all be pleased with me." For a moment there was a shocked silence round the table. But then Norma added: "However, I can give

you my solemn assurance that all the classic ingredients for an economic upturn are now in place."

I was greatly relieved to hear this.

Wednesday

Mrs Thatcher has done it again. She really is, in my judgement, out of control. I heard on the Radio Two News that she has demanded that the pound should be devalued. What a stupid thing to say! Does she not understand the technicalities of the new ERM system, which we are now part of, thanks to her government? The rules are that you cannot devalue unless Mr Kohl gives his permission. I was about to ask him when she ruined everything by saying that I ought to, which obviously means that I cannot now do it.

Anyway, I was greatly relieved to hear later in the day that the pound had gone down on its own, with no help from anyone.

Thursday

Will Mr O'Donnell ever get it right, I am beginning to wonder? Last night I had to give the very important morale-boosting speech to launch our election campaign. Mr O'Donnell had chosen for my theme an honest admission that the economy was in a terrible mess. "It might get a few sympathy votes," he said, as he handed me my script. All went well until I got to the middle of p. 97, when I came to a passage which described everyone who is attacking the Government as "Dismal Johnnies". Fortunately I spotted this just in time, remembering that in Cabinet, whenever Norma Lamont uses the word "Johnnies", everyone giggles. So I hastily improvised and changed in to "Dismal Jimmies", which I thought was a rather inspired, off-the-cuff reference to the last Labour Prime Minister! "Mrs Thatcher never managed to make a joke like that," said Chris, when he heard what I had said on the next morning's Today programme, which he rather disloyally, to my mind, still listens to.

Friday

There was a not particularly pleasant moment today when we saw on the News that my friend Mr Bush had nearly died while he was in Japan. "That's terrible," said Mr Mellor. "Just imagine the country being taken over by a faceless and inexperienced nobody." At this point everybody bent double, and I assumed that they were all suffering from an attack of gastro-enteritis, like Mr Bush. However, I was greatly relieved to discover that they were all merely laughing, though I am not quite sure why.

Monday

The most important choice of my life now faces me, as I told the Cabinet at our brainstorming weekend at Chevening.

"Is it to be May?" asked Mr Hurd.

"No," I said firmly. "The BBC have asked me to appear on Desert Island Discs' 50th anniversary in March." I thought everybody knew this, but many in the cabinet are rather slow on the uptake despite the advantages of having been to university. Still, some of them were not unhelpful in suggesting the choice of gramophone recordings. Mr Waldegrave proposed "We don't want to lose you, but we think you ought to go", which he said was a rousing marching song from *Oh What a Lovely War*. Mr Rifkind said the most appropriate song was from *My Fair Lady*, called "Why Can't A Man Be More Like A Woman?". I am not sure he has got that right. I made a note in my new Radio 5 notebook to ask Norman about this.

My friend David Mellor, who is very highbrow, said that I should choose something classical. "One of Bach's Three-Piece suits, perhaps," Mr Hurd ventured and everyone laughed at him. Poor Douglas.

However, I have made my own decision on the records. I will decide nearer the time. I am my own man, oh yes.

The choice of book is not inconsiderably easier. It will be

either *Wisden 1959–60* as I have always said or, as Jeffrey Archer suggested to me on the phone this morning, *The Jeffrey Archer Omnibus* (four best-sellers from the Master Storyteller in one handy volume).

The luxury is obvious. To be completely free of Mrs Thatcher and never to hear her voice ever again.

Tuesday

The date of the General Election has been officially decided by the *Daily Telegraph*. It is 9 April, which is a not inconsiderable relief to everybody. As for the Budget, it is to be on 10 March, which is also a great relief. *The Telegraph* did not, however, say what was going to be in the Budget, so I immediately went next door to ask Norma Lamont whether he knew. I told him that I did not want there to be any accusations of trying to bribe the electorate, and that it was very important that we should be seen to be exercising wise and prudent stewardship insofar as it lay within our prerogative. "Quite so, Prime Minister," Norma replied. "We have never shrunk from unpopular measures. Why don't we cut income tax for everybody in the country?"

Wednesday

One of the most exciting things about the election is seeing the brilliant new posters which my friends Chris and David think up every day to beat the Labour Party. This morning they showed me their latest effort, which looked quite like the previous one except that this time the huge bomb was the other way up. On the side of the bomb it says IF YOU VOTE LABOUR, YOU'LL DIE. "But surely," I said, "Labour wants to ban the bomb?" "Quite right, Prime Minister," said Chris. "A very good point," said David. It is a good thing I am here to stop them making silly mistakes, and

obviously neither of them minded being criticised since they were both laughing quite loudly as they left the room.

Thursday

A man called Mr Peter Brooke came to see me today. He offered me his resignation, which I politely accepted. "No, no," said Mr Hurd. "You are meant to refuse it." Sometimes it is very helpful to have someone around who knows about the protocol. I therefore insisted that Mr Brooke should stay on to do whatever he does, whenever it is he does it. When I asked Mr Brooke why he wanted to resign, he said that he had sung "Clementine" on television without knowing the words. In my judgement, that does not appear to be a matter to resign over. For instance, if I was asked to sing "Shrimp Boats Are A-Coming" by Miss Alma Cogan, which is one of my favourite songs, I would not get much beyond the first lines: "The shrimp boats are a-coming, the shrimp boats are a-coming, there'll be dancing tonight, oh yes."

On the way home from the House of Commons I saw a huge poster showing a bomb and saying WATCH OUT FOR SUSPECT PACKAGES. This is a much better attack on the Labour Party than the last one. David and Chris will be glad they listened to my advice.

Friday

Today is D.I.D. Day. I am due at Broadcasting House at 11 o'clock and Mr O'Donnell arrived in plenty of time to give me my list of records and what to say in between.

It looks very interesting indeed and I look forward to hearing the records, many of which are new to me. I did however recognise what Mr O'Donnell had highlighted with a yellow pen as THE JOKES — i.e. "I suppose I could escape easily from the island in a balloon because I am the Prime Minister." This is an old favourite of his, as are all the others.

Ms Lawley was at first very pleasant but she kept intro-ducing an unnecessary and not in any sense pleasant note by asking me to thank you-know-who for making me Prime Minister. Ms Lawley was remarkably bossy about this and reminded me in no small measure of the woman who I do not ever mention. I certainly do not think Mrs Thatcher had anything to do with me getting on Desert Island Discs!

Sunday

As I listened to the programme at home I thought some of

the recordings seemed not entirely judicious. For example, they left out the singing in "Land of Hope and Glory", which rather spoilt it, and also I could not understand why they had chosen Frank Sinatra when my favourite singer is Alma Cogan, especially "Shrimp Boats Are A-Coming".

Later I asked Mr O'Donnell about this who told me that the tune was significant because it was called "The Best Is Yet To Come".

I said that since it was the eighth record, there WAS no more to come. Mr O'Donnell can show remarkable obtuseness for a man with a Double-First.

Monday

Today I am due to fly out to meet Mr Yeltsin, or perhaps he is to fly in. As Mr O'Donnell says, the important thing is to have a photograph of us both near an aeroplane.

I explained to the Cabinet that the situation in Russia was in my judgement very grave. The economy was collapsing with unemployment rising, inflation increasing and their new leader in need of all the support he could get.

My friend Chris Patten gave a snigger, which I considered inappropriate in the circumstances. I put this down to the strain of thinking up a different poster every day to attack the Labour Party.

Sunday

I was very considerably surprised when I opened the *Sunday Times* this morning to learn that Mr Kinnock had been a Soviet agent. My friend Chris rang me in great excitement. "Isn't it great news about Kinnock?" he said. "You must go on television at once and say how much you deplore these attempts to smear the Labour leader." "But I thought you said it was good news?" I replied. "Of course it is, John — but you are meant to be above that sort of thing." I have no idea what he meant. Sometimes one has to admit that Mrs Thatcher was right when she said: "It's a funny old world."

Monday

What an extraordinary coincidence! No sooner has Mr Kinnock's reputation been ruined than suddenly Mr Ashdown is revealed to have had an affair. "This is getting worrying," I said to my friend Chris. "Both the other leaders have been smeared. Do you think it will be me next?" Chris gave me one of his funny looks and laughed. "Oh no, John," he said. "I have this funny feeling that somehow you'll be OK on this one."

Tuesday

It seems that Mr Ashdown is more popular than ever as a result of this unhappy business about his secretary. My friend Chris rang me up to say: "Have you seen the bad news —'86 Per Cent Back Ashdown Says Polls'. It looks as though this one's rather backfired on us. You've got to do something." Luckily, just at that moment Mr O'Donnell came in with the script of a special interview I was to give to Radio One. I was glad to see that I completely sympathised with Mr Ashdown and that I too had been through a rocky patch in my marriage which would get a lot of sympathy with the voters." "Oh, when was that?" I said. "Don't you remember that time when you were Foreign Secretary and you didn't know where any of the countries were. You had to work late every night for several weeks reciting all their names to Mr Waldegrave." It all came back to me — "France, Spain, Estonia, the disputed territory of Nagorno-Karabakh." It's funny to think that in those days Mr Waldegrave knew more than me. But now I know at least one thing that he doesn't know — although he will find out very soon, oh yes!

February

Wednesday

Today is the big day of my interview on Radio One! I think they are all getting to know me quite well at Broadcasting House because I am there so often! I was very considerably delighted when they rang me up to say I could choose four records of my choice to go with my interview. Now is my chance to have all the songs that Mr O'Donnell wouldn't let me use on Desert Island Discs. They are "Shrimp Boats Are A-Comin' In" by Alma Cogan, "The Party's Over" by Frank Sinatra, "I'm A Three-Time Loser" by Rod Stewart and "Hello, Goodbye" by the Beatles.

Thursday

I am glad to say that my choice of songs has proved a great success with the listeners and the newspapers have praised the way I sympathised with a man whose political career is unfortunately, as I put it, "completely finished through no fault of his own". My friend Chris rang up to say there had been several more offices burgled in the House of Commons — all, as it happens, belonging to Labour MPs. "Perhaps," I suggested to Chris, "we should have a new Charter to protect Labour MPs from being burgled." Funnily enough, when I said this there was an odd click and a mystery voice started to laugh in the background. Clearly we had some sort of crossed line.

Friday

I am on top of the world, having very considerably humiliated Mr Kinnock in the House of Commons. And it was on TV! My wife Norman and I watched it on the 6.00 News as we ate our Italian-style Chicken Principessa from M&S. We were lucky enough to catch it again at 7, and then at 9 and 10. Mr Kinnock obviously thought he had trapped me with a trick question, when he asked:

"When is the recession going to end?" Quick as a flash I jumped to my feet and read off my clipboard: "Asking that question shows that you are not fit to run this country." All our people cheered and cheered at this brilliant reply, and afterwards Mr Mellor gave me a wink and said, "Well done, John. Looks like those old shrimp boats of yours could be coming in at last."

Monday

Today I had a visit from an American man called Mr Quayle. He said he was a friend of Mr Bush and wanted to talk to me about GATT, which I naturally assumed was a kind of life assurance. I told Mr Quayle that I already had a very good policy with the Prudent & Provident Society, a considerably respected firm offering a wide range of benefits on retirement. Not that I am thinking of retiring. Oh no. But American salesmen can be very persuasive and I ended up signing a piece of paper just to get rid of him.

Tuesday

Mr Hurd tells me that my meeting with Mr Quayle yesterday was a diplomatic triumph. All the newspapers from the *Daily Mail* to the *Daily Telegraph* carried the headline MAJOR'S TOUGH TALK WINS OVER BUSH ENVOY. GATT AGREEMENT IN SIGHT. Oh yes.

I was enjoying in no small measure my lunch, consisting of a Marks & Spencer Kiwi Fruit and Tuna On Wholemeal Granary Bread Sandwich, when I heard on the one o'clock news an announcement that the German economy was in recession. I at once rang up my friend Helmut Kohl to express my sympathy for this terrible news. He was so distraught that he could not remember who I was. Just then, my friend Chris ran in, shouting: "Great news about the Germans, John. Their economy is up the spout. That means they're in recession just like us." "What on earth do you mean?" I asked. "Our recession ended at the end of last year. Norma Lamont said so. You really must pay attention, Chris, or we will not win the election." He gave me one of his funny looks.

Wednesday

Today in Cabinet everyone seemed to be excited about a secret weapon to win the election. When I asked what it was, my friend Mr Mellor said: "John, it's got everything we're looking for — it's got charisma, leadership and great powers of oratory. It will knock Kinnock for six." "Really, David," I said, "there is no need to flatter me. I'm not Mrs Thatcher, you know." Then Mr Heseltine ruined it by standing up and saying: "OK, gentlemen, I volunteer to be the secret weapon." They all clapped.

Thursday

Today I had another great success over Mr Kinnock in the House of Commons. Mr Kinnock asked me whether I would condemn the increase in the long-term unemployed. I leaped to my feet, holding my special grey ring-pull folder from Rymans, and said, off the top of my head, without even looking at my notes: "Yes sir, no sir, three bags full sir." Even the Labour Party cheered at this brilliant reply.

Then it was Mr Heseltine's turn, but I am sorry to say he did not do too well. In point of fact, our side was so disappointed they stood up shouting and waving their order papers for several minutes.

Friday

Norma Lamont has come up with a brilliant idea for winning the election. At a special top-level strategy meeting this morning he told us that he could ensure victory at the polls by a single stroke. "We'll give away billions of pounds in tax cuts," he said.

"But Norma," I cautioned, "you told me we hadn't got any money to give away."

"No problem, Prime Minister," he replied. "We'll borrow it."

Why did Mrs Thatcher never think of something as clever as this? I bet she wishes she'd had a Chancellor as clever as mine.

Saturday

Today I travelled north to Scotland which is a by no means inconsiderable distance from London in my judgement. Apparently there are lots of people in Scotland who think they are in a different country. This is nonsense, as I saw with my own eyes. When we crossed the border we were completely unaware that we had so done. There were no guards, no wall, no passport control and no duty free, as Norma Lamont pointed out.

I made this observation to a gathering of all the Conservatives in Scotland — well over 212 people, all crammed into the hall my friend Chris had hired. It was a great success and many of them stayed right to the end.

Monday

Today is another red-letter occasion in the run-up to the General Election. I have decided to introduce a Freedom of Information Charter. However, I was furious to read about this in the newspapers.

Who told them? It really is pretty disgraceful that you can't keep anything secret these days. I will have to introduce a new Secrecy Charter to prevent this sort of thing happening again. NB: I have written this entry in invisible ink.

March

Monday

My friend Chris has come up with another brilliant poster for the election. It shows two enormous boxing gloves, with the slogan LABOUR'S DOUBLE WHAMMY. I must admit that when I first saw it, I was a little puzzled. But Chris explained it was to appeal to "the ordinary geezer in the road", who would know what a whammy was. "Well," I asked, "what is it?" He gave me one of his funny looks, and said he would find out by lunchtime.

Tuesday

Today is one of my favourite days in the year, Pancake Day. Oh yes. Mr O'Donnell came in and said: "We're all going to have our pancakes in the street." I was not sure about the point of this but we went outside and discovered hundreds of

photographers wait-
ing for us. Norma was
carrying a big frying
pan and I carried the
mixture in a bowl.

"Where's the
lemon?" I asked, and
everyone for some
reason looked at me.

Mr O'Donnell's
other idea this week
was to persuade my
wife Norman to give
an exclusive inter-
view to the *Daily
Mail* about her
dreams. She said she
often has a nightmare

about a huge grey snake wriggling about in her bed reading
Wisden. In the article a psychologist said: "This gives a clear
indication that the Tories will win the election."

Wednesday

Every Wednesday in my Chelsea Football Club Executive
Appointments Diary is marked with a large green star. This
means that it is time for a new Charter. Today is Railway
Day. As I told the Cabinet last week, there are a very considerable number of commuters in the country and their votes
could be in no small measure important for deciding the
election. It would be prudent therefore to win their support.
"How can we do that?" asked Mr Rifkind, in his funny Scottish voice. "Easy," said Norma Lamont. "We give them lots of
money. It's what we do for everyone else." They all cheered,
except for Mr Waldegrave who as per usual was trying to be
clever in his toffee-nosed Old Etonian way. "How is all this
going to be paid for?" he asked. "Easy," I said, having a
brilliant idea. "We'll put the fares up."

Thursday

My friend Chris rang up in great excitement this morning.
"We've won!" he shouted in jubilant tones. I was considerably
surprised to hear this as I had not been aware that the election had taken place, but it turned out that he was talking
about the cricket in Australia. "Oh yes," I said. "I have been

awake all night listening to it on my Walkman. I expect the hissing noise is what makes Norman dream about snakes." Chris gave me one of his funny laughs, the sort he gives when he and Norma Lamont are having one of their jokes together. "By the way," I said, "have you solved the mystery of the Double Whammer yet?" But the line had already gone dead.

Friday

Business as usual. Item One on today's Cabinet meeting agenda, at my insistence, was the meaning of our new policy about Whammies. Mr Hurd suggested that it might possibly have something to do with bridge. Kenneth Clarke thought it was something to do with what drummers did in a jazz band, and annoyed me considerably when he tried to illustrate his point by banging on the table with one of my favourite biros. Norma Lamont said that as far as he was concerned he had not had a Double Whammy since he stopped over in Bangkok on the way back from some conference. Finally Chris read out a briefing document from our advertising agency Hargleby, Bogle and Pratt which explained the term: "Double Whammy. American rap slang expression, short for Double Whamburger, a type of grilled processed meat in a bun, served with cheese, onions etc." Everyone cheered at this. What a genius Chris is! Hamburgers are very popular, and so will we be! Oh yes.

Tuesday

Mr Lamont's Budget has been a great success. His picture is everywhere and it is front-page news. This couldn't be better timing when we are about to have an election! It is also in no small measure fortunate that Norma's Budget is going to make every-one better off. I congratulated him on this coincidence. He

laughed and winked at me. "You could say it is a budget for jobs," he said. "Ours."

On the subject of jobs, I have decided to reduce the number of Cabinet posts. By at least one, and I think Mr Waldegrave knows what I am talking about.

Wednesday

Mr O'Donnell tells me that I have chosen a new theme tune for our election campaign.

"The Labour Party has Brahms," he said. "So we are going to have Persil."

"Oh good," I said. "It is one of my favourite adverts, and Norman says it washes grey out completely."

Monday

I am delighted by the success of Norma Lamont's budget. He promised me that he would not bribe the public to win votes and this morning's polls show he has been as good as his word. We are 3 points behind.

Mr Smith has made an absolute idiot of himself with his first budget as Labour Chancellor. We always predicted Labour would make a mess of it when they got in, and here is the proof. He has foolishly put his foot in his own goal by offering lower taxes for 98 per cent of the population.

I told the Cabinet that this was clearly just a cynical bribe which the electorate will immediately see through. "Is that why Labour has now gone 5 points ahead?" asked Mr Waldegrave, in his sneery public-school voice. I am seriously beginning to think that there is one cut the Health Service could benefit from! Oh yes.

Tuesday

Today Chris told me that our secret weapon to win the election was ready to go. He took me out into the street where there was an enormous Greyhound bus, with the slogan written on the side WHAM YESTERDAY AND WHAM TOMORROW BUT NEVER WHAM TODAY UNDER LABOUR. Unfortunately there was not room for all these words, so the last bit had to be written very small. Inside they had built a replica of my office down to the tiniest detail, even including my *Daily Telegraph* Wallmap of the World and the old peanut butter jar in which I keep my special biros, one for each day of the week. There is also a fax machine, a toilet and a very large television. As we headed

up the M5 Chris
switched it on and
there was Mr
Heseltine waving
his arms about
and saying that
Mr Kinnock was a
raving lunatic who
should be locked up.
Everyone cheered
wildly.

"Well, John, what
do you think of our
secret weapon?"
Chris asked. "I think
it is a very nice bus,"
I said.

Wednesday

Today I launched our manifesto at a special press conference. It is very much my own work, although in fact it was
written by other people. On the front there is a picture of
what Chris calls "the new caring face of Conservatism". It is
me, with my new glasses! Inside there is plenty to read, with
full details of all my Charters, now over 100 in all. There is
even a complete timetable for all the BR trains in the country, with the names of who to complain to if your train is
more than 2 hours late! After they played the Persil tune by
my friend Andrew Lloyd-Webber, I was ready to answer
questions from all the journalists, but Chris explained that
there was no time, I was going to submit myself to a full
grilling by the public later in the day.

Sure enough, that evening I was taken to a Conservative
Club in Hemel Hempstead to face a barrage of hostile questions from all sections of the local Conservative Party. I had
to sit informally in the middle of lots of people, and then the
interrogation began with a question from my friend Jeffrey
Archer, who just happened to be in the audience. "Don't you
agree that it would be a disaster if Mr Kinnock won the
election?" he asked. Well, you'd think a close friend could
come up with an easy one to start with. Afterwards he explained that he could not afford to be seen sucking up to me,
and told me that I had handled it brilliantly, once I had got
into my stride.

Thursday

I am to be the star of a film! A very famous director called Slazenger has decided that he wants to make a film about my life. It is to be called *The Journey*, and it is about a man who rises from the slums to become prime minister, just like in a Jeffrey Archer story. The first part of the film is about me going to Brixton to see if the house where I used to live is still there. In fact I know it is, but I had to pretend that I didn't know, so that when we came round the corner I could say: "Look, there it is. My old house. It is still there. It is. Vote Conservative." Then the second half of the film showed me driving back in the car to Number 10 Downing Street, which is the house where I live

now. It is rather shorter than a normal film, but it will be shown all over the country. My friend Chris said: "If that doesn't win us the election, nothing will." Labour are now 7 points ahead in the polls.

Friday

Imagine my not inconsiderable surprise when you-know-who (Mrs Thatcher) turned up on the same platform as me at our big meeting — incidentally it was our best yet and everyone stood up and cheered at the end. But I said to Chris: "Why is that woman here? I thought the Party had got rid of her because she was going to lose us the election."

Chris smiled and said: "That's right, John, but we are doing so well now that we can afford to show a little kindness. It meant a lot to her to hear them all cheering you when she finished her speech." Chris can be very thoughtful in his way.

Monday

I refuse to get downhearted in any measure by the fact that we are behind in all the seven polls published today. The

Daily Mail has surely got it right when it says KINNOCK
HASN'T A HOPE as its main news story. These people have
been in journalism for a very long time, so I am sure that
they know what they are talking about. And, moreover, why
would Mr Heseltine look so pleased with himself if we were
going to lose? He really is a morale-booster. The other night
he came up with a real cracker. He said that if Labour won
"we would get our Kinnocks in a twist". This was nearly as
good as my joke when I said that, if Labour won, I would be
having "Nightmares In Downing Street". This was suggested
by my friend Jeffrey Archer, who said it was based on the
name of a very popular new film and was what he called a
"sound bit" — i.e. the bit that they pick up on the soundtrack
of the TV.

Tuesday

The Labour Party has really scored an own goal this time!
They have produced a film about a little girl who goes deaf
because of our health cuts. Mr Waldegrave called a press
conference to say that the film was jolly unfair and worse
than anything Hitler did in Nazi Germany.

For once I am beginning to think that Mr Waldegrave is
getting the hang of this electioneering! As a result of his
hard-hitting press conference, we are now only 9 points
behind.

Wednesday

Today I am going to unveil another secret weapon. My
friend Chris tells me that it will turn the tide, not of course
that it needs turning, as the *Daily Express* confirmed today
with its headline MAJOR HOME AND DRY — ASHDOWN
PROBABLY A POOF. Anyway, at today's big rally I am going
to show that I can be "Mr Nasty", if I deem it appropriate in
my judgement. Oh yes. Mr Woodward, the young man who
has been brought in to run my very successful campaign, has
given me a little wooden box to get up on when I make my
speeches. "That will put you head and shoulders above Mr
Kinnock," said Chris, giving Mr Woodward one of his funny
winks.

April

Thursday

This morning David Mellor bounded on board the battlebus, waving a morning paper and shouting: "Great news, John. We're 20 points ahead on the polls. Mr Kinnock has conceded victory."

"That must be as a direct result of my soapbox idea," I said.

However, David burst out laughing — "Ha, ha, ha. April fool! We're 10 points behind."

I like to think that I have as good a sense of humour as the next man, but I did not find this particular joke amusing in any way whatsoever.

Friday

I notice that Norma Lamont has not been pulling his weight in this campaign, to my somewhat annoyance. After all, it was him who got us into this temporary economic downturn and it is time he stood up to answer prepared questions about it from selected Tory supporters. I brought this up at our meeting this morning, as we were going round the M25 in the battlebus. Mr Woodward, who used to work on *That's Life* and knows all about how to make people popular on television, explained that some people were "camera-friendly" and others, through no fault of their own, were not. "Norma Lamont is a no-no," he said. "So is Waldegrave and so is Selwyn Gummer."

I must have looked surprised at this, because he continued: "Particularly Gummer. No one wants to see a boring little nonentity with glasses who has nothing to say and who loses votes every time he opens his mouth."

"No, they don't," I agreed firmly and for some reason they all started laughing — no doubt to relieve the tension.

Saturday

My friend Chris produced his trump card which he has kept up his sleeve until the last minute. It is a brilliant TV broadcast in which we tell everyone what the Labour Party's phone number is. Just to annoy them!

It worked brilliantly! Hundreds of people rang Mr Kinnock up, pledging support, giving money and complaining about our broadcast.

Who says we haven't got any Big Ideas left?

Sunday

Tonight I went to Wembley. But not to watch football with Mr Mellor. He says there will be plenty of time for that after Thursday. Oh no. It was Celebrity Night, when some of the biggest names in sport and showbusiness pledged their support for our campaign.

For example, there was Trevor Bailey, and a pop star called Bill Wyman, and Gordon Banks, who played in goal for England, and Patrick Moore of TV fame and many more. My friend Jeffrey Archer, whom I recognised instantly, introduced me personally to all of them. Trevor Bailey made a very funny joke when we shook hands. "Who are you?" he said, pretending not to know who I was. The idea obviously caught on, because everybody I met used the same joke. This became increasingly not very funny, in my judgement, but it made for a relaxed atmosphere.

Monday

Guess who phoned me up to offer me his support? David Owen, no less!

Now I know we are going to win. I had a long talk with him and expressed my considerable sympathy with his current predicament. Being alone in the wilderness when you have once been centre stage as leader of a Big Party.

"Oh yes," he said. "I knew you would sympathise. We have a lot in common."

Wednesday

We are in no way worried about the outcome of the election. It has been a brilliant campaign, and on the battlebus I made a little speech thanking everyone. "You have all played your part. And even if we were to lose," I said, "nobody would be to blame."

"Yes he would!" they all shouted in unison and pointed at me. I didn't understand the joke, but they all laughed like at a pantomime and it showed that morale is very high indeed.

Thursday 9 April Polling Day

Today is the big day! I have to decide which way to vote. Having carefully considered all the options, I have come to the conclusion that I will vote Conservative! When my wife Norman and I arrive at the polling station in Huntingdon, the press men are waiting. "How are you going to vote?" they all shout. "Labour," said Norman, in one of her very good jokes. Then they asked me and I said, "I am going to vote for the winning side." "He's Labour too," said Norman, in another of her jokes. Inside the polling booth, in fact, it was a very easy choice. My name was on the paper in large blue letters, but Mr Kinnock's was not. This shows that he cannot possibly win in my judgement.

Later we went back to London, and outside Downing Street there were a number of large vans, marked "Removals". "It must be something to do with the television," I told Norman. She seemed very confused by all this media attention, and I heard her say to one of the drivers, "Can you be careful with the tea chest marked 'Crockery'?"

To relax we went next door to a drinks party with Mr Lamont. I had the feeling that someone had died, because everyone in the room looked very sad, and Norma himself kept talking about "a tragic loss". Other people reassured him there was nothing anyone could have done, as whoever it was had been "a hopeless case".

However, after a few drinks they all went into the next room to watch the television. Since it was already 11 o'clock, I thought it was high time that Norman and I went home to bed. "I've got a lot to do in the morning," I told our host. "Not necessarily you haven't," said Mr Waldegrave, who happened to be standing nearby. I think he may have had too many of Mr Lamont's special "Double Whammy" cocktails.

Friday

When I woke up I turned on my bedside radio and heard Mr Redhead saying that I had won the election.

Norma was already up and when I went downstairs I found her unpacking lots of boxes marked "Kitchen", "Dining Room" and "Lounge". There is no doubt that she has been under a lot of stress in the last few weeks. Then there was a ring at the door and in walked my friend Chris. "Isn't it considerably satisfactory news?" I said. "It has all gone exactly as I hoped." Then I noticed that he was crying, and Mr O'Donnell explained that unfortunately Chris could no longer be my friend, as he had lost his seat. "I am very sorry," I said, "but I am afraid that there is no place for losers in my new government." Chris gave me what may well be the last of his funny looks.

Saturday morning

I am my own man at last! That is what it says in a very interesting article in the *Daily Telegraph* by Mr O'Donnell under the pseudonym Charles Moore. Now I can choose my own Cabinet. The minor appointments were easy. I have decided that Norma Lamont should stay as Chancellor of the Exchequer, as a reward for his success in getting the country out of recession. Mr Hurd will have to stay on as Foreign Secretary, because he is the only one who knows where all the countries are without looking at the map. David Mellor came in to say that he would like to be Minister for Free Tickets to all the things we go to together, such as football matches and cricket, not to mention operas which Norman likes. "Oh yes," I said. "That is the sort of fresh thinking we are going to have from now on."

Then Mr Baker came in, and giving me his considerably annoying smile, he said: "A million congratulations, John, we owe it all to your brilliant leadership. What would you like me to do?"

"I would like you to resign," I said, giving him a smile of my own! "The time has come to clear out all the dull men in glasses whom Mrs Thatcher appointed to suck up to her."

Saturday afternoon

Next to come in was Mr Heseltine who for some reason was looking very depressed. I thought I would cheer him up by saying that I was going

to give him the job he had always wanted. "I doubt it," he said, looking even more depressed.

Then came the bit I was really going to enjoy most, when Mr Waldegrave arrived. He looked very considerably nervous, and said: "I know what you're going to say, Prime Minister. I entirely accept that you had no alternative but to sack me."

"Oh no," I said. "I've got something much better up my sleeve for you than that. Something which really matches up to all your talents. You are to take charge of a new department, where you will have the very important job of answering the telephone to all the people who ring up to complain about their trains being late. And in addition I want you to take full responsibility for making the tea when really important people like the new Health Secretary come round." "And who is he?" asked Mr Waldegrave. "Wrong as usual," I said. "He is Mrs Bottomley, a woman who is going places or as Mr Lamont puts it 'a real little goer'."

After he had gone, I had quite a good laugh. Oh yes. It is fun being Prime Minister.

<u>DEAR BILL</u>

The last irregular correspondence from the husband of
the *former* Prime Minister to a golfing friend

December 1990 – April 1992

Denmarg
Eventide Estate
Dulwich

Dear Bill,

Do thank Daphne for the floral tribute: don't tell her that they got sent to Number 11 by mistake. We only got them when little Norma Major crept in to ask if it was all right for her to measure up for their G-Plan. (By the way, if you see Maurice, tell him the housewarming's off as the beefy lads from Hearthguard plc said they cannot guarantee the back of the building in the event of things getting out of hand, as they believe they would, having read the guest list.)

I can't say the past few days have been entirely untraumatic. I finally bit the bullet and strolled into the Mem's bedroom at two a.m. on the night of the first ballot to find the old girl rehearsing her number for Halitosis Hall the following afternoon. She was three-quarters of the way through the Quart of Old Smuts Seventy-Year-Old South African Whisky which Terreblanche gave me to bring back after my last trip, and was gripping one of Carol's old rag dolls round the throat to represent Pillock. "I fight on, I fight to win!" she was repeating in a low growl. "If I do not secure a majority at the second ballot I shall at the third, and failing that at the fourth!"

I coughed politely to indicate my presence. "Ingham has two hundred definite pledges, and that number will be doubled when they hear my speech toomorrow, Denis!" she cried. "Another ten years!" At this I cleared my throat and helped myself to a largeish measure of the good Terreblanche's electric soup. "Up to a point, old girl," I temporised, "but let us consider the Party's interest. Surely our watchword at this late hour must be Screw Heseltine."

The Boss winced at his name but did not interrupt me. "Now then, you may remember at the Golf Club the case of Barmy Winnifrith." The little woman did not seem to recall those historic events of 1949 when Barmy was under threat from the Committee for excessive drinking at meetings of the Ways and Means Group. Sniffing the way the wind was blowing, he made an emotional speech, announcing his resignation from a club of which he was not worthy to be a member. His resignation was accepted with regret. The following day, however, the Secretary and the rest of them felt they'd been absolute swines, what would the club be without Barmy prostrate on the floor every night? They must make amends. They therefore unanimously re-elected him. Four months later he burned the clubhouse down, but everyone agreed it was a good way to go.

M. had been listening to my tale with unwonted attention, and I could see that I had planted a shrub in her mind which might well bear fruit. Sure enough the following morning she announced that she was heaving in her clogs.

Flowers then began to arrive by the lorry-load, Cecil P. came round and sat weeping openly in the hall, and there were a few people like Baker who rang up offering their condolences. But to M's increasing irritation there was no deputation begging her to change her mind. "No matter, Denis," she observed in a somewhat dampened mood as she waited for the limo that would spirit her down to Halitosis Hall. "When my people in the constituencies hear the news they will rally in their thousands."

The old girl was clearly banking on Pillock putting the boot in good and proper during his No Confidence Palaver, thus creating a huge wave of sympathy and support. Not for the first time, however, the pea-brained Welshman let her down, not knowing what an ecu was in answer to a question from his own side and turning the whole thing into an end of term charade. I think at this point the waverers finally registered that it didn't matter a bugger who was leading her side, anybody could knock spots off Pillock, why didn't they all have a go?

M. understandably was fit to be tied and yours truly got it well and truly in the neck with a hurricane-force Krakatoa that fair took the plaster off the ceiling. However, there came a point in the catalogue of my shortcomings when she suddenly appeared to run out of steam, reminding me of the time when we were trying to get Maurice sectioned at Deal after the episode at the Del Mar Pavilion. The old boy put up a spirited resistance until that little shrink Wheatcroft gave him a shot of tranquilliser in the buttock whereupon his eyes unfocused and he said he would come quietly.

Moments later she was on the blower to every one of the backbenchers saying that unless they voted for Major she would see to it that they were deselected by their constituency parties, all of whom were fiercely loyal to her and would kill at her command. This seemed to do the trick and Wonderboy romped home in the Allcomers' Stakes.

I don't know if you've ever met this Major bird, but he's very like that man at Gieves & Hawkes who gets the material down for shirts. Very polite, nicely spoken, very keen to please. Not perhaps one's first thought as a successor to Gladstone and Disraeli, but there you are. Boris, who entre nous is a bit of a snob, rang up the newspapers and said he'd overheard the Boss saying she was staying on as back seat driver. I naturally assumed that would scupper him, but his bandwain of ex-yuppies and Tarzanophobes was not to be stopped.

By the way, if you read in the *Sun* that I am terminally ill and that was the true reason for her decision to resign I would treat it *cum grano salis*, Gascoigne Pees my MI5 friend having been employed for the last few days to put round a few face-savers. He was out and about already to spread some dirt about Heseltine and his ladyfriends, but none of the reptiles took the bait.

Meanwhile D.T. covered in dust and grime was providing photo opportunities for hacks carrying out eleven years' worth of empties from H.Q. I was rather surprised in the middle of this exercise when one of Maurice's Pakistani Removers beckoned me over and told me I had a personal call. Blow me down, Major from next door, can he have a word in my ear? How was I feeling, Mr Thatcher. Nice morning, chilly for the time of year. Hoped my lady wife was well. Talking of which, the job of Ambassador in Washington could well be going begging. He knew she was a very good friend of Mr Reagan and Mr Bush and several other American gentlemen. Would M. care to slip it on for size? I pointed out that M. had made the self-same offer to Sailor Ted on his sudden retirement from office with a view to humiliating him, and that I thought the offer might well be taken in bad part by the Memsahib. Major said "Oh deary me", and thought he'd have to go back to his drawing-board. Forty seconds later, blow me, Major on the phone again. How would I feel about my wife being made Governor General of Australia on an open-ended basis? It was a very key job, particularly now that the Australian gilt market was looking so buoyant. I would have a chance to see some good cricket, and did I know that there were more bars to the square mile in New South Wales than anywhere else on earth? I professed ignorance on this score, but agreed to pass on his message.

I hope our saunter round with the clubs is still on for Thursday. The form when you arrive is to press the red button on the little brick post before the barrier, and don't be alarmed if a man with a gun points it at you. Once you're cleared by showing him the enclosed electronic tag, which he has to put through his computer, you will be allowed to drive up to the gates. All being well the infra-red light will come on and release the mechanism to withdraw the metal teeth in the road and the gates should then open if you tap the attached code into the panel on the right of the entrance. However don't put your arm too far out as there is a hidden guillotine device to deter loiterers. Once inside the gates, do not, repeat DO NOT, get out of your car as you may run into a bit of strife with the police dogs. They're very friendly when they know you. The easiest thing really is to ring me on your carphone — remember it's 081 — when you're outside the front door.

Somehow I don't think I'm going to enjoy my retirement as much as I had anticipated.

Yours in limbo,

DENIS

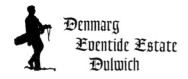

Denmarg
Eventide Estate
Dulwich

DECEMBER 1990

Dear Bill,

Thank you for your case of Krug '08 in celebration of my entering Debrett. I hope you and I will have an opportunity one lunchtime of knocking it back, with Maurice if he has been released into the community by then.

The whole charade started at the Boss's final highly emotional chinwag with H.M. the Q. The D. of E. took me backstage for a snort in the billiard room while the little women dabbed at their noses and wondered what they were going to do without each other. "Well, Thatcher," said the old seadog. "You're a lucky bugger. I only wish someone would gang up on my old woman in a dark alley and toss her on the dustbin of history. What's it to be?" I said I'd like a large brownie. "No, no. What did you fancy in the way of gongs? We'd been thinking along the lines of Duchess of Grantham. You could choose your own courtesy title. They've got a list of names downstairs. Take your pick."

I quite fancied the idea of a Dukedom. I've seen the way they treat that old grog-blossomed party in the plus-fours at Huntercombe — Knockmadoon? Westminster? There's no doubt at all you get quicker service at the bar if you happen to be a Duke, even the Pro calls him "My Grace" and is always kneeling down doing up his shoelaces and breathing on the toecaps. However this was not to be.

In the Limo on the way home I mentioned H.R.H.'s offer to the Mem and the temperature went down by a good hundred and fifty degrees. "Et tu Denis?" I could see she was very displeased. "You too trying to kick me upstairs? That awful place? Pym, Carrington, Waddington? That purgatory where the lost souls of politicians sit waiting for release? No, Denis, no. I am still a young woman, younger than General de Gaulle when he retired from the army. Gladstone was 102 when he formed his final government. There may well come a day when they will remember me and call me back to resume supreme power." You see the sort of thing I have to put up with, Bill, but the old girl's obviously been under a lot of strain.

A couple of days later, however, the topic re-emerges over breakfast. Man in a helmet arrives at the outer gate, a packet from the Palace. It turns out to be a catalogue very kindly sent round by the Duke showing all the different gongs and sashes that are on offer. First few glossy pictures show various old grotesques hobbling about in Cowpat hats including that old bugger who used to traipse

113

round the dirty book shops. However, these were all overstamped "Regret no Vacancies, H.M. the Q." Second on the list was their special offer Order of Merit, a limited edition restricted to "twenty-four Achievers of Distinction in all walks of life". One available due to death of old actor. "That's the one for me," cried the Boss, marking it with her biro. "Look, Sir Winston had one, it is just the very thing." I cast an eye over some of the other owners, and it seemed to be a very rum sort of a bunch. Mostly eggheads and that fiddler Johnny with the talkative wife who's always standing on his head. However, the little woman seemed perfectly satisfied and said: "Let's find something for you, Denis. I know, here's just the thing. Mark will love this, leave it to me."

So it was I discovered that I was to be Sir Denis Thatcher Bart, i.e. keeping the bloody thing warm for the boy Sir Mark. What really sticks in my craw is M. refusing to be Lady T. So the next time you see us at your Rotarian Rats and Vipers Lunch the Johnny at the door will doubtless bellow out "Sir Denis Thatcher Baronet and Mrs Margaret Thatcher" thus spreading confusion and suggesting the boy Sir Mark is not legitimate.

As you will have seen in the blatts we're on the move again. You may remember I bought Denmarg from that friend of Maurice's with the green Roller after a rather heavy lunch, and I'd taken a good deal of trouble installing the air-conditioned liquor store. Golf course just down the road, very sound neighbours including a nice Greek man in the arms business, American widows etc, everything seemed hunky dory. But even on the way there with M. I could tell things weren't right. She started drumming her fingers on her hatbox and looking out at the traffic in Brixton. "I thought you said it was only fifteen minutes from the House of Commons, Denis! How can I do my bit in the lobbies and help poor little Mr Major to find his feet from this distance?"

Worse was to come. On our arrival I must have put the plastic card in wrong, and metal teeth rose from the surface of the road to puncture all four tyres. Shortly after that an ear-piercing siren went off, a barrier came down, crushing the top of the car, and armed men appeared. It was therefore a bit of an anti-climax when I led M. in through the front door to the scene I had prepared, with Boris in his new white coat standing by the gas log fire with a bowl of Twiglets and sherry cooling in an icebucket, the legend over the mantelpiece

"With best wishes for your Retirement from Mohammed and Slizi Fayed".

M. is still haggling with Central Office over the size of her Alimony Pay-Off, talking in the high millions with a view to buying something a little more central. If you need to reach me I shall be spending the next two weeks at the R.A.C. under the name of Mr Gottlieb.

Yours away in a manger,

DENIS

Denmarg
Eventide Estate
Dulwich   FEBRUARY 1991

Dear Bill,

Forgive the long silence, but as you can imagine life has not exactly been a bowl of cocktail cherries. You ask about Hoppo's Eightieth. Ever since the balloon went up, our American Cousins have been trembling in terror at the thought of using public transport as far as the corner store, so one happy result is that we had the Concorde to ourselves going over, except for that TV man with the bags under his eyes who does the breakfast show. (The stewardess told me he practically lives on board and keeps his own toothbrush and shaving mug in one of the overhead lockers.) Maurice's travel agent also managed in the circs to get us a very good deal whereby they gave us a champagne dinner if we accepted a free ticket.

With my mind on a possible Retirement Home for Margaret, I was naturally keen to see how well Hoppo had done for himself in this line, and I must say Rancho Magnifico at Santa Harmonica is very salubrious. If you picture Dozy Willis's hacienda in Majorca, where we stayed the time Maurice dived into the empty swimming pool, multiplied by six that will give you a dim idea of the sheer glory of it. We got picked up at the helipad by the Old Cowboy himself, driving his electrified golf buggy, and driven out to our personalised bungalow on the estate — one of ninety — complete with its own miniature golf course, swimming pool, massage parlour and drive-in cinema. On the way over there the old boy, who appears at first sight to be quite sane, held forth about the need for what he called a Positive Attitude to the Golden Harvest Years.

I hoped the Boss might be lending an ear to this, but she gazed out of the window, only occasionally delving in her bag for a handful of pills which she crunched grimly as the former President expanded on this theme. "My good friend Dr Billy Graham has put it very beautifully in his little work *Get Rich with Jesus Today*, a copy of which you will find by your bed in the ranch house. 'There is no more beautiful sight in God's World than a wise old man, his tasks accomplished, his face marked with the lines of kindliness and experience, his head powdered with silver, asleep in his chair after a good lunch.' "

Such figures inevitably tended to predominate at the Big Eight-Oh Barbecue that evening at the Hail To The Chief Ranch House. I think the youngest person present was that crooner with a wig in the Mafia, who was persuaded to sing later on. I drew the short straw at dinner and got a poolside seat next to the Emaciated Spouse, our only other neighbours at table being a very old comic, also in a wig, called George Burns, and Madame Blavatsky, a clairvoyant who told me she'd had an office in the White House and used to advise the President on propitious days to get out of bed. Burns, who smoked a cigar all through the turf 'n' surf chowder that followed, eventually said: "If I was in bed with you I'd get out of it pretty damn quick."

Margaret sat through the whole grisly business with a vacant expression on her face, even when her neighbour, Bob Hope, who must be ninety if he is a day, rinsed his false teeth in the champagne and did an impersonation of a very elderly chimpanzee. Hope really put his foot in it when the heavy drinking got under way, when he asked the guests to raise their glasses of Passion Fruit Low Calorie Knockout to our honoured guest, the Prime Minister of Great Britain — "long may she reign". At this Margaret produced a handkerchief and blubbed for the rest of the evening.

As you will gather from the foregoing, the transition from workaholic to alcoholic has not been an easy one. Do you remember when Humper Willoughby was suddenly persuaded to take early retirement by Glaxo? One minute he was a ball of energy, burning the candle at both ends — breakfast meetings after his jog, on the go, like the famous egg, from arsehole to breakfast table. Then, wham! One morning he wakes up, filofax blank until the Day of Judgement. Next time we saw him he was pushing a zimmer frame round the East India and Sports looking like Maurice after one of his electric shock treatments.

I won't say the Boss has quite reached that stage yet, but life in the flat in Belgravia — very commodious, porter on the door, couple of sheiks upstairs (all very quiet) — is proving very edgy. She still gets up at four in the morning, bangs about a lot with suitcases, waiting for Farming Today to come on, and by the time I get down for breakfast she's usually pretty livid. "You'll be off to the House of Commons, I imagine," I tried saying yesterday. "You don't want to miss the big debate on the Gulf." Instant Krakatoa. She was not going to set foot in the place. Those ungrateful swine. The humiliation of sitting next to Heath. "Come on, old girl," I tried. "You always liked it there in the old days." After that she used several very explicit words and I have no idea where she picked them up. The gist of it was that it was all my fault for being such a useless husband, always drunk, only interested in my business friends. A real husband would have kept her informed of the vile conspiracies going on behind her back, would have counselled and advised. Then she started blubbing again and took some more of her new pills.

If she goes on like this I'm toying with the idea of asking Maurice round. After all he has a history of mental instability in the family and might be able to suggest some wheeze.

Yours amid the encircling gloom,

DENIS

~~Denmark~~
~~Eventide Estate~~   SOMEWHERE
~~Dulwich~~   IN BELGRAVIA   MARCH 1991

Dear Bill,

Thank you for your welcome home crate of London Gin, which I hope you were prudent enough to obtain at pre-Budget prices. I'm sorry you were rather given the run-around by Mr Al-Sabbagh, the porter, but he has strict instructions to direct all callers to misleading addresses in the northern suburbs as a security measure. If you come again, press the bell marked Gottlieb and I will come straight down.

With regard to the coded enquiry contained in your greetings card, I think the whole trouble started in Washington. The Americans have never grasped our system of doing things, and when M. was summoned over by Basil Bush to collect her gong, practically all of them were under the impression that she was still sitting behind the big desk. The little woman, having touched down in a state of near collapse with depression and bad indigestion from swallowing Dr Gebler-Davis's happy pills, immediately perked up, and came out of the White House like that Frankenstein's monster they have on the TV when he's had five million volts put through him on the slab.

It was just like old times. Senators toasting her right and left — if it hadn't been for her Bush would never have gone over the top, shades of Winston, hands across the sea, Rule Britannia and three cheers for the Red White and Blue. Small wonder, then, that by the time she got on the TV with their local equivalent of Sue Lawley, the old girl was on a pretty good high, and sounded off in no uncertain manner about the Tory party being a lot of spineless shits who chickened out when the going got rough; the Boche would steam-roller us if we went into Europe and little Major was trying to turn the clock back to the bad old days of fudge and smudge. All thoroughly sound stuff, received by the Yanks with general rejoicing and a run on British Exports.

Seconds after she came off the air, one of those lecture agencies rang the studio offering her an open-ended Coast-to-Coast tour on any subject she chose and asking her to name her price. Even I was invited by the Denver Temperance League to get up on my hind legs for $200 and warn the youth of America about the peril that lurked in the screw-top bottle. Margaret asked the Boy Mark to fix a deal, which he did in exchange for a sliding scale of the gross, at £27,000 a throw.

When we got back the phone immediately started to ring. I picked it up as we entered the flat, only to recognise the fruity tones of Old Oystereyes. Could he toddle round for a chat, he hadn't seen us for so long, there was so much to catch up on, how was our little grandson, etcetera etcetera? M. smelt a rat at once, and received the elder statesman with a measure of icy reserve. Undeterred, the old boy sank into a chair and launched into a well-rehearsed tour d'horizon with special reference to her American comments, which he said has sparked off a good deal of chatter in the tearooms. She must find it difficult to realise this, but there were even wild rumours that she was planning some kind of come-back. He, of course, knew as well as she did just how preposterous such speculation must be, but for the good of the party it might be ahem aha the best policy to put a stop to it once and for all by accepting a peerage. The House of Lords was in crying need of leadership, and those who said that Mark was an unworthy recipient of such hereditary honours should be put in their place now by a grateful acceptance of the title Duchess of Grantham.

"Willie, Willie, how sweet of you!" Margaret beamed in her most terrifying way. "You always had my good and the good of the Party at heart, and you are a dear kind man. Where did you leave your coat? It has turned quite cold and it would be terrible if you caught a chill at your age. Let me see you to the door."

When the old boy had gone I ventured to say that a peerage sounded quite a good wheeze, thinking the while that it might at least get her out of the house for the day and provide her with someone else to sink her teeth into other than yours truly. At this, however, Scuds were aloft within seconds, all targeted on myself. Had I not given any thought to the future? Already her chosen heir had betrayed her and sided with Heseltine; her cherished Community Charge was in ruins; before long it would be free milk and orange juice, child benefit through the roof, Helmut Kohl eating Apfelstrüdel at Buckingham Palace with the Queen every other week. What would the public do then? They would have no alternative but to elect a Labour government. "And then what, Denis?" I was about to say that with any luck I would have snuffed it by that stage, but an eerie gleam shone in her eyes and I realised she was not listening. "Then, Denis, like Arthur of old, slumbering in the cavern under the hill at Glastonbury, I will hear the trumpet call and awake. I will return to slay the dragon of Socialism!"

It is very depressing, and although you or I might dismiss it as delirium tremens, the old girl has got a good deal of evidence on which to base her delusions. Sackfuls of letters arrive by every post begging her to return and sort out the chaos, and my MI5 friend Gascoigne-Pees whom I saw at the RAC the other day asked me if I'd like them to put it about that little Major had a black woman in Streatham who dressed him up in chains and threw custard at him. Early days, but I'm not sure I like the way the wind is blowing.

Yours in the shadow of the tomb,

DENIS

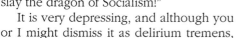

Dedmans
Eventide Estate
Dulwich SOMEWHERE IN BELGRAVIA   MAY 1991

Dear Bill

Forgive the longish silence, but I've been rather overwhelmed by having the little woman hanging about the house all day while I'm trying to work the microwave. I have managed to fill a sufficient number of Highland Spring bottles with G and T to keep going pro tem, but the stress is beginning to tell.

When the news got out that we were moving to Chester Square I got a call from Maurice P. offering his pantechnicons free of charge in exchange for a plug on the News at Ten, and since then it's been pretty good chaos. A Mr Tariq appeared, with a string of letters to his name and various degrees in removal technology, claiming to be Maurice's chief packer. Everything down to fag-ends resting on the side of ash-trays and bits of used soap was wrapped up and crated by willing, if swarthy, hands, and that, to date, is the last we have seen of it. Maurice thinks it may have gone to Chester, but my hunch is that it will soon appear in the current police exhibition of stolen objects near Birmingham.

As I think I may have told you, the Boss has been in a very volatile state since the unfortunate events of the autumn, and I had the gravest doubts about the wisdom of her opening her heart to a Miss Latrompe of the American magazine *Vanity Bag*. Admittedly there's hardly a soul, from the road-sweeper up, to whom she has not opened her heart in the past few months, but this was for mass circulation. I thought it prudent to sit in on the tête à tête, pretending to be worse for wear and dozing off a heavy lunch.

"It mush have been a truly terrible trauma for you, Lady Thatcher!" the Manhattan harpie began. "Would you say your whole world was shattered into a million pieces like a priceless Lalique stained-glass mirror?" This was enough to turn on the waterworks despite the hosepipe ban, and M. sobbed loudly for some moments before answering. At this there was a sustained thumping on the wall, and the anguished voice of our neighbour saying some of them were trying to get a bit of sleep. I don't know whether you know him, Bill. A mad violinist Johnny who stands on his head before breakfast and has a very talkative wife. He turns out to be very touchy about noise.

"And how does it feel, Ma'am, to be able to spend more leisure time with your precious dear ones?" "Sod that!" erupted Margaret unexpectedly, giving yours truly a fairly shirty look. "Home, as my husband knows, is somewhere you come when you're unemployed. Look at him. A vegetable! I've warned him about lunchtime drinking but he takes not a blind bit of notice. Now," she continued, drying her eyes and fixing Miss Latrompe with a hypnotic glare, "write this down exactly as I dictate it. Mrs Thatcher is still vibrant and full of energy, and she has no intention of being forced to take a back seat... " I deemed it prudent to wake up at this point, an unwise move as it turned out, as I was instantly cindered by the gamma rays and ordered to take myself off to the RAC. As I cleared the door I listened with sinking heart as M. began to lambast poor little Major for dismantling the Poll Tax and being "so wet you could wring him out".

I hope you got my pc from Jo'burg. The Boss, as you can imagine, was on Cloud Nine, having received a personal guarantee from de Klerk that there would be a red carpet at all the major venues, personal motorcade and liveried outriders, the freedom of the city and a platform wherever she went to lecture the world on her Destiny and the folly of opposing her inevitable return to power. He even laid on crowds of demonstrators shouting "Maggie Out!!" to remind her of the old days.

While the Boss was being feted by the Boers, I made a rather half-hearted effort to contact your friend the Diamond King to suggest a tie-up with Maurice's Pic-Crap Jewellery consortium. Somebody's got to make some money now the Boy Mark has launched himself as a literary agent and effectively fouled up the Memoirs Deal.

Yours in the red,

DENIS

66 CHESTER SQUARE
LONDON SW1

JULY 1991

Dear Bill,

As you may have gathered from the blatts, I was "away on business" when the little woman announced her shock decision to leave the back benches and finally join me in the Peerage. So, to tell the truth, I'm not 100 per cent au fait with what led up to it.

I think the seeds were probably sown during our highly profitable trip to the US of A. The night before her big Chicago speech, I found myself sitting at dinner next to a Mr Jason Hammerhead Jr, Vice President of Hammerhead International Communications. Possibly I was rather over-egging the nog on the subject of the Boy Mark and his ill-fated efforts to raise the wind on the Boss's Memoirs, her hopping rage at our blue-rinsed sailor's beating her to the post by having his life-story serialised in *Hello!* (Daphne's favourite magazine, isn't it?) when shazam, Herr Hammerhead gripped me by the back of the neck, slapped a contract on the table, spirited a large old-fashioned fountain pen out of thin air, and drew my unsuspecting hand over the dotted line marked signature.

M's big barnstorming speech went down like the proverbial cup of c.s. with the Yanks, to whom the name Jacques Delors conjured up only some dim memory of a dirty French film star in the twenties, and she got back to the Abraham Lincoln Suite of the Mobil Park Lane Hotel in downtown Chicago not in the best of moods. During the flight to New York I mentioned the enthusiasm of Mr Hammerhead, and on our arrival in Manhattan she rather reluctantly agreed to take the seventy-five storey lift ascent to his apartment in the Lloyd Webber Tower. Here, behind a huge desk, the walls adorned with photographs of Reagan, Marilyn Monroe and that Mafia singer with the hairpiece who, it now transpires, would you believe it, was the emaciated spouse's bit on the side, sat Jason H., dangling a set of solid silver worry beads and talking very big indeed. Performers, he argued, showing his fine white teeth, had to be seen to be performing. What did she think she was doing in Chicago? Margaret began to answer this, but he cut her short. "Conciliatory, my ass," he growled, leaping from his desk and striding about the room in highly-sprung gym shoes. "We are talking megabucks, baby." I saw Margaret was not taking this very well, but the delicately-stubbled Mr Hammerhead remained oblivious to her mien. "High Profile. Combative. Bette Davis. Zsa Zsa Gabor. Trouble!"

"Mr Hammerhead," the Boss intervened, rapping her fingers on the ivory desk. "You do not appreciate my position as a back-bencher..."

"Don't give me that backbencher crap," cried our American friend. "We're looking at world rights. It could be six million bucks up front. You're a big international figure now, Lady Thatcher. You don't want to be hanging around in your House of Parliament like that red-faced has-been Heath."

At the mention of our seafaring friend, the Boss's expression changed and she agreed to give careful consideration to Mr Hammerhead's views and to be in touch.

On our return to our new £100,000-a-year lease here in Chester Square, I could tell that M. was increasingly irritated by the calls waiting on our telephone answering machine urging her to exercise restraint and clemency for the sake of party unity, and asking her to various out-of-town social events on the day of the big Euro-debate. I was not surprised when on the day in question she went down to Halitosis Hall and delivered a vicious attack on Major, pledging her full support for his policies. The following day, when Major flew off to his latest Euro-junket, she rang up the Press Association, summoned all the reptiles round to the doorstep, and announced that she was giving up the back benches in order to speak her mind on a whole range of international issues. Late that night I was shaken awake by the telephone ringing on my bedside table, and I overheard a gravelly American voice congratulating her on her coverage. "Thank you, Mr Hammerhead, you are so kind," she soothed, "though I assure you headline-grabbing as you put it was never in my mind. Yes, I'll fax you a specimen chapter on Monday."

If you and the Major could turn up at Fortress Dulwich some time after dusk on Friday I think we should be able to get the remainder of the booze out of the air-conditioned store and safely away to the Major's friend's garage. Until that time of night there's always the danger that Maurice or the other estate agent Mr Goldsack will ring up at short notice to bring some prospective purchaser round to wonder at the oaken fitted kitchen and en suite Master Bathroom. To date there have not been many punters. The first was quite a hopeful geezer from Idaho, keen fan of the Boss, who wanted to dismantle it brick by brick and reassemble it somewhere over there in a Theme Park. Then there was a shifty-looking Arab johnny, sent round by the Al-Fayeds, with a bevy of women in nose-pieces, but the Boss vetoed them on the grounds of their insanitary habits. After that I had to wait in all morning for a Mr Odinga, a huge Coon in a Rolls Royce, who seemed quite promising, but then I noticed when he blew his nose the boot polish came off on his hankie, and sod me if it wasn't some lager lout from the *Sun*, with a sidekick dressed in a fez and stick-on moustache, who asked to go to the lav. I caught the little monkey with lots of those white umbrellas up, taking photos of Margaret's Whirlpool Bidet.

Yours borne away on the ever-rolling stream,

DENIS

Denis Executive Estate
Dulwich SOMEWHERE
IN BELGRAVIA
OCTOBER 1991

Dear Bill,

Forgive the long silence but we've only had a kitchen table and a couple of buckets in the way of furniture at Chester Square while the builders have been in. Needless to say Maurice's contractor friend Mr Rick has had us over a barrel, bewildering us with all sorts of technical talk about girders and stress quotients while he has continued to fleece us unmercifully. The so-called Estimate went out the window months ago, and there have been endless variation orders for everything from bullet-proof glass in the window of the downstairs toilet to full soundproofing of the entire house to prevent the Boss's tantrums from disturbing that fiddler Johnny next door when he's standing on his head doing his morning meditation.

Meanwhile all hell has been let loose over Margaret's Foundation. Without so much as a by your leave, the Boy Mark took it into his head to appoint himself chief fundraiser and the old girl's manager, rocketing round the world, embracing sundry crooks and other beneficiaries of Margaret's regime, grinning in an insinuating manner behind his dark glasses and saying as much as "We scratched your back, now you can bloody well scratch ours".

Apparently one or two of the more sinister coons, chinks and wogs approached cut up pretty rough, threatening to put the police onto him, and in one case releasing Rottweilers. All of which has caused unwelcome speculation about the Boy Mark's activities, and with M. no longer in a position to keep it out of the papers there is some consternation both at Downing Street and chez nous as to what will happen once the reptiles go to work.

Boris, who is coming in part time to wait at table as he is now persona non grata in the former Soviet Union, told me that according to the KGB's files, Mark had been using M's name for years to drum up business in the arms trade, offering various shoddy merchants of death what he described as "the fast lane to the Boss". The Savoy Hotel is mentioned as a possible location for these "social encounters", and what is particularly irritating is that my own name has also been mentioned in this context, suggesting that I was up to exactly the same game, e.g. the Major's planning permission for his housing development near High Brooms and Maurice's consignment of industrial chloroform — i.e. Nerve Gas for Saddam two days before the balloon went up in the Gulf.

After a good deal of headscratching in the Cabinet Room about the possible deleterious effects of the Thatcher Foundation blowing up in a shower of shit on the eve of an election, the powers that be have decided to try and cut the old girl loose and let the whole thing drift out to sea. The plan is to rush through an Earldom for the Boss, who will become Her Grace the Countess of Grantham, all as speedily as possible before awkward questions are asked about her son and heir, His Grace the future Earl of Backhander.

How does yours truly fit into all this hasty ennoblement, you may enquire? Already, as you know, a widely popular elevation to the baronetcy, I will remain plain Sir Denis Thatcher Bart, thus distancing myself from my repulsive progeny, in so far as that is possible.

What, you may further ask, is the point of the Thatcher Foundation in the first place? I asked Mark about this when we were briefly on speaks a week or so ago, and from his sneering and dismissive remarks I gained the impression that it was something that had been thought up by his Miami accountant, a Mr Lazlo da Silva who advises him on "disappearing" money.

Social life has been of necessity cut to a minimum, but I did have a very agreeable Sunair Algarve Minibreak with the Major, Maurice, and his new girlfriend who runs a pet food shop in Tenterden. The air-conditioned limo that Mother Flack sent to the airport for us broke down outside Cintra, and we got a lift after having taken a certain amount of drink in a local wineshop from an evil-smelling lorry transporting live lambs in contravention of EEC regulations. Maurice passed out in the back and was quite badly trampled. He is now being sued by the driver for the death of several of his sheep who seem to have passed out due to the alcohol fumes. The Widow sent you her best regards and wondered whether you remembered Rosita who used to work in the dry cleaners and did the gypsy dancing at that nightclub called the Blue Baboon. Funnily enough I met her son, a slightly backward figure pushing forty, who was the spitting image of your good self.

Keep in touch,
Yours as the shades lengthen,
DENIS

B O S T O N
HYATT
INTERNATIONAL

APRIL 1992

Dear Bill,

I can't tell you how sorry I was to have to v.s. on your seventy-ninth shindig at the El Morocco Rooms in Deal. I gather from the Major that a good time was had by all, though I'm sorry to hear about Maurice's little accident in the ensuing fire.

As you may have gathered, I had hoped to be well and truly out of all the ghastliness this time round. I've had my share of bad eggs over the years, not to mention offal and one occasion a brown-paper bag full of sheep's excrement thrown by a disgruntled hill farmer. Even the Boss, I think, had determined to come to America, earn a few spondoolicks to pay the central heating bill in Chester Square, and generally shake the dust of the septic isle off her Max Rayne high heels.

First morning of the campaign, sure enough, a bunch of flowers in appalling taste wrapped in cellophane and distressing blue plastic ribbons was delivered to the flat with a little card saying "Best wishes for your trip to America, yours affectionately, J. Major." The message was clear, to me at least. The Boss was to be out of the way, while little Mr Hercules did his number on the high wire. By all means, as far as I was concerned, and I hoped he'd break his bloody neck.

"Poor John," the Boss observed with a patronising inclination of her head. "How very kind, when he must have so much on his mind. Now, where is my in-flight word-processor?"

We were not due to leave for another three days, and all seemed to be going as planned, at least as far as we were concerned — little Major admittedly making a total prat of himself by rotting Kinnock instead of rallying the troops for the millennium — when one day there was a sudden rat-a-tat-tat on the knocker soon after midnight.

Having no domestic staff whatsoever, yours truly staggered to the door and began the lengthy business of switching off the various alarms, drawing bolts and unlocking locks.

Hunched on the doorstep with his collar turned up and looking v. sheepish was the new Party Chairman, that big thug Patten. I don't know whether you've seen him? Looks like some sort of barmy hayseed leaning on a gate with straw in his hair. Never really one of us, and a Left-Footer to boot. Could he come in? A bit of a crisis.

By this time the Boss was roused, her hair in curlers, an icy smile on her face. "Dear Chris, how lovely to see you! What can be the trouble?"

It was a sorry tale that our bucolic friend had to tell. The opinion polls were sliding away from us, no reason to panic, but John was wondering whether she would care to join him on the platform for their big rally? We were by now sitting in the drawing room, and Margaret put her head on one side in a thoughtful manner. "Let me just get this right, Chris. My understanding of it was that I was to resign as I was an electoral liability. Is that correct?" At this Patten looked rather nonplussed and began muttering under his breath about hasty and unthoughtout decisions. "Well, Chris, *am* I an electoral liability?"

"Er, Margaret," he began, "John feels, and I feel too that it's time to bury the hatchet, if only for the sake of party unity... "

"You haven't answered my question," she persisted, switching on the low-level gamma rays, at which I observed our corpulent friend begin to smoulder. "It seems rather odd, doesn't it, to invite an electoral liability to be on the platform?"

You've probably seen those pictures, Bill, of chaps in Inquisition Days being stretched to unnatural lengths under the gaze of a beady-eyed bishop or twain. Such was the fate of poor Patten. He left the house at 3 a.m. a broken man, but with the Boss's assurance that she would indeed appear at the rally.

So, once again, the old girl scented blood, and yours truly was whirled along in the wake as of yore. Grisly reptiles on every hand snapping away, microphones thrust down one's throat, repulsive old ladies pushing forward to squeeze one's fingers in a sticky grip, all the horror of the mob. M., I need hardly say, rejuvenated, eyes gleaming, nostrils wide, making Major's present lot look like bloody amateurs.

With all this hullabaloo, I was assuming that America was off and I could join you for your beano, but it was not to be. A very odd thing happened. I had just taken my treble-strength nightcap and was negotiating my way up the three stairs to my bedroom, when the old girl suddenly appeared before me like that woman who washes her hands in the Shakespeare. "Denis," she intoned, "I want to talk to you."

I say this was odd, because I can't honestly recall an occasion for a good twenty years when the old lady has chosen to confide in me. Groggy as I was from a bottle or two earlier in the evening and the lateness of the hour, I am not sure I can remember her precise words, but the upshot was that not even she could prevent the *Titanic* from going down on this occasion.

"You and I are going to America, Denis. We have done the best we can, we will not be here to witness Mr Major's humiliation." "Thank God for that!" I think I interrupted — and may have sung a few bars of "California here I come". "Be quiet, Denis, there's a love. Of course the Party will be very angry. They will seek revenge. Poor John, they will want another leader."

"Well," I began, pulling myself together, "what about Hurd? Snooty bugger, I agree, but a safe pair of hands." Even at the time I was vaguely aware that my speculations were not being as well received as they might have been, but I blundered on. "Or Patten, I suppose? Or Heseltine? A total shit, I agree, but with some notion of leadership..."

M's voice cut through me like a chainsaw. "Don't be ridiculous, Denis, you are obviously drunk."

I must have passed out pretty soon after that, and was haunted with terrible nightmares. We were back at Number Ten, Mr and Mrs Kinnock had been executed by the SAS, Heseltine was in prison awaiting trial for treason, and Margaret had in some way altered the Constitution to stop any more elections taking place. I wonder what it all means?

M. is out at a lunch and I'm all alone in the hotel room feeling suicidal. I know we used to laugh at that sort of thing when we were younger, but do you think that shrink friend of Maurice's — Weidenfeld? Lambton? no matter — would be prepared to give me a session on his sofa? Not a word to any of the boys, obviously.

Yours in the valley of the shadow,

DENIS

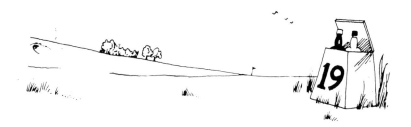

ALSO AVAILABLE FROM
PRIVATE EYE • CORGI

COLEMANBALLS 6

Another incredible crop of
cobblers from Private Eye's
Colemanball column.

£2.99

REAR
COLUMNS

Collected Diaries
of the Famous.

£4.99

POETRY
CORNER

Collected Verses
From Thirty Years
Of Private Eye.

£4.99

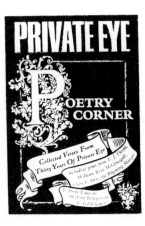